The Energy Education Experts

Thank you for your purchase of *Understanding Today's Electricity Business*. If you wish to purchase additional copies of this book, please visit our website at www.enerdynamics.com. Or call us at 866.765.5432. Volume discounts start at as few as 25 books.

Please also look for this book's natural gas companion, *Understanding Today's Natural Gas Business*. As with our electric book, this presents a comprehensive overview of the natural gas industry in simple and easy-to-understand language. It is the perfect primer for those new and not-so-new to the industry, and a valuable reference for years to come.

We also invite you to experience other learning opportunities available from Enerdynamics. These include in-house seminars, self-paced online training, and social media opportunities to stay connected such as our *Energy Currents* blog and *Energy Insider* newsletter. Learn more about all these products at www.enerdynamics.com.

Understanding Today's
Electricity Business

By Bob Shively and John Ferrare

The Energy Education Experts

3101 Kintzley Court, Suite F
Laporte, CO 80535
866.765.5432
www.enerdynamics.com

Enerdynamics Corp.

Enerdynamics is an education firm dedicated to preparing energy industry employees for success in a challenging environment. We offer an array of public and in-house educational opportunities including classroom seminars, online seminars, and books. We can be contacted at 866-765-5432 or info@enerdynamics.com.

Please visit our website at www.enerdynamics.com

About the Authors

Bob Shively brings 30+ years of experience in the gas and electric industries to Enerdynamics' educational offerings. As President of Enerdynamics, Bob has advised and educated some of the largest energy industry participants on issues including business strategies, developing competitive electricity markets, and implementing new technologies such as renewables and Smart Grid. Bob has also served as Vice-President of eServices of Sixth Dimension, Inc., an energy networking company where he worked closely with retail marketing and ESCO companies. Bob began his career in the energy industry at Pacific Gas and Electric Company (PG&E). At PG&E Bob held various positions including Major Account Executive to some of PG&E's largest end-use customers and Director of Gas Services Marketing where he was responsible for product development and sales for the company's $1.5 billion Canadian pipeline project. Bob has Master of Science degrees in both Mechanical and Civil Engineering from Stanford University. He is a frequent energy industry speaker and is co-author of Understanding Today's Natural Gas Business and Understanding Today's Electricity Business. Bob is an active member of IEEE and is a registered professional engineer in the State of California.

John Ferrare has worked in the energy industry as a marketing and communications specialist for over 25 years. He began his career with Pacific Gas and Electric Company where he was integral in developing the marketing group for the company's Gas Services Marketing Department. Since that time, he has also worked with PG&E Corporation and PG&E Energy Services in the development of marketing and communication strategies. In 1995, John joined Enerdynamics to manage its educational services. In this role, he has helped create a comprehensive program to educate 600 utility employees on the changes brought by deregulation as well as the core classes currently offered by Enerdynamics. A graduate of Northwestern University's School of Speech, John has also developed and teaches a seminar on how utilities make money.

ISBN 978-0-9965285-9-7

Edition 7.0

The authors of this book wish to thank Dan Bihn, Chuck Sathrum, Karen Shea, and Greg Stark for the immeasurable improvements they suggested in reviewing drafts. We wish to thank the analysts at the Energy Information Administration whose data is used throughout our book. And Tim Collins whose extraordinary illustrations often tell so much more than our words ever could.

John would also like to recognize Alex and Leo, whose barks, hugs, licks, and genuine concern and affection offered considerable motivation during the long hours of editing this document.

Bob thanks Carol for her support and love, and thanks Jed and Tarah for understanding that his computer is necessary for something besides playing online games.

We owe a huge debt to Amy Robinson-Russ whose painstaking attention to the grammatical details the rest of us missed will certainly make this book an easier read for all!

And finally, we wish to thank the tens of thousands of participants in Enerdynamics' seminars and programs, who in the last 20 years have taught the authors more than we could ever have imagined.

CONTENTS

What you will learn:

- An overview of today's electricity marketplace

- The units used to measure electricity

- The importance of electricity in today's society

- Electric usage levels in the U.S. and the world

- A brief history of the electrical industry

1

SECTION ONE: INTRODUCTION

Today's Electricity Marketplace

A world with an insatiable appetite for electricity awakens to a new era. Technological advances rapidly expand the possibilities of what electricity can do and how it can be created. Consumers demand access to a continually advancing array of products and services based on the ready availability of reliable electric supply. In some regions, regulated utilities dominate the market and are the only electric providers available to consumers. In others, all customers are free to choose their electric supplier and service providers compete vigorously. Government regulation, once the stable backbone of the industry, struggles to keep pace with technological and marketplace developments and the conflicting demands of varied market participants. And concerns over environmental impacts create a push to change traditional generation sources. Meanwhile, rapidly developing societies across the globe clamor for modern conveniences, causing worldwide demand to double every 25 years. This is today's electric marketplace.

It's hard to imagine, but just over 140 years ago Thomas Edison was drawing up the papers to create the Edison Electric Light Company. At that time, the electric lights and motors that Edison would power had yet to be invented. Now our society would scarcely exist as we know it without the ubiquitous movement of electrons known as electricity. As we move ever deeper into the information age, virtually all our activities are dependent on one commodity — electricity.

And paralleling our increasing dependence on electricity is an electric marketplace marked by rapid change. Market structures that remained stable for more than a century are being radically transformed. The staid vertically integrated utility is, in many areas of the world, being forced to separate into distinct generation, transmission, distribution, and retail services companies. Generation and retail services are being opened to competition. In some areas, customers who never thought twice about their electric service now shop for retail suppliers as casually as they do cell phone service providers. Some consumers are becoming prosumers by generating and storing power that can be sold back into the grid. And caught in the wake of this turbulent industry restructuring are the fates of many corporate enterprises, some whose future prosperity suddenly seems to be in question.

The technology of electricity continues to evolve as well. In the 1990s, the improvement of gas turbine generation technologies enabled gas-fired generation to provide system flexibility and, in many cases, more cost-effective supply with less environmental impact than existing utility generation units. In the 2000s, wind generation became a viable large-scale technology followed by a significant cost decrease in solar photovoltaic generation in the 2010s, resulting in significant growth of renewable power. As this book goes to print, battery storage systems are increasing in capability and decreasing in cost, promising options to manage supply and demand balances in new ways. Ongoing technology innovations suggest continued evolution. One future scenario might be a centralized supply model based on low-carbon resources such as utility-scale renewables, new nuclear generation technologies, storage, and natural gas with carbon capture. Another might be a distributed supply model based on resources such as rooftop solar, fuel cells, batteries, flexible loads, and/or combined heat and power located at customer facilities. Or the future may be a combination of both centralized and distributed supply resources. High voltage direct current transmission might supplement the existing transmission grid with a backbone system that can move large amounts of power many thousands of miles with low losses. And revamped distribution grids using new technologies may transform the distribution system into a services network enabling transactions among multiple service providers and consumers or even between consumers in peer-to-peer transactions.

In this book, we'll take an in-depth look at this rapidly evolving industry. We'll begin with an overview of U.S. and global electricity use and some history on how we've gotten to where we are today. Next we'll look at what electricity is and how it gets to consumers, followed by who electricity consumers are and how they use electricity. From there we'll examine in depth the three physical sectors of the delivery system — generation, transmission, and distribution — and how these sectors are operated. We will study electric market structures and explore who does what and how these market participants are organized and interact. Then we'll open the doors to regulation and deregulation and take a look at how the electric industry has evolved to where we are today. Next we'll study the dynamics of the market and how participants attempt to make money and manage risk. And finally, we'll sneak a peek into the future and speculate on what exciting changes may lie ahead.

As you may know, the electricity business is filled with acronyms and industry-specific jargon that will be important for you to understand. For this reason, we suggest you

A WORD ABOUT UNITS

We cannot effectively discuss electricity without referring to the units by which it is measured. So it's extremely important that you clearly understand the following concepts.

Units of demand/capacity

Demand reflects the instantaneous amount of work required to perform the function desired (e.g., creating light or physical force, powering a microchip, etc.). Similarly, capacity reflects the instantaneous ability to provide energy required to do work (e.g., generation and transmission capacity, etc.). Demand and capacity are measured in units of watts, kilowatts, megawatts, or gigawatts:

1 kilowatt (kW) = 1,000 watts

1 megawatt (MW) = 1,000 kW

1 gigawatt (GW) = 1,000 MW

As an example, consider an 8-watt compact fluorescent light bulb in your living room lamp. When you turn the lamp on, the bulb creates a demand of 8 watts. And in order for this electricity to be supplied to the bulb, 8 watts of capacity must be available at the generator and along the entire path between the bulb and the generation source.

Units of energy/usage

Energy or usage reflects demand or capacity multiplied by the amount of time that demand or capacity is in use. Energy and usage are measured in units of watt-hours, kilowatt-hours, megawatt-hours, or gigawatt-hours.

1 kilowatt-hour (kWh) = 1,000 watt-hours

1 megawatt-hour (MWh) = 1,000 kWh

1 gigawatt-hour (GWh) = 1,000 MWh

Let's consider again our living room lamp. The 8-watt bulb it uses to light your living room uses 8 watt-hours of energy if you leave it on for one hour. If you leave it on for a 24-hour period, it would consume 192 watt-hours (8 watts X 24 hours), which is the same as .192 kWh.

Of course, that's just for one bulb. An average suburban home in the United States (with a single air-conditioning unit) has a peak demand of about 3–5 kW, with an average demand of approximately 1 kW. Peak demand refers to the greatest amount of electricity required at any given moment. Typical average monthly usage for this home would be about 900 kWh. Total U.S. consumption is almost 4 trillion kWh per year, which breaks down to about 11,500 kWh per person. Peak demand in the U.S. is approximately 770,000 MW.

begin your study with a look at the glossary and the list of acronyms found at the end of this book. We also suggest you refer back to the glossary whenever you find a word you don't understand. Once you are comfortable with these terms, feel free to study the information contained in this book in any order that makes sense for you. Good luck and have fun!

Electricity in Modern Society

In most cases, economic growth of a country or region is linked to growth in electricity demand. And similarly, a decline in the economy results in a decrease in electricity

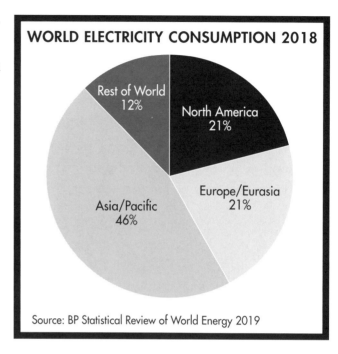

WORLD ELECTRICITY CONSUMPTION 2018

Rest of World 12%
North America 21%
Europe/Eurasia 21%
Asia/Pacific 46%

Source: BP Statistical Review of World Energy 2019

consumption. But as societies learn to use electricity more efficiently, electricity usage grows (or declines) more slowly than economic output. In the U.S., electricity usage typically grew by 5% or more per year during the 1950s, 60s, and 70s. In the 80s and 90s growth declined to 2 to 3% per year. In the 2000s it fell to about 1% per year and since 2010 usage has been flat. Interestingly, while the U.S. population grew by 69% between 1961 and 2011, electricity use grew by 416%. But for the seven years between

2011 through 2018, U.S. population grew by 5% while electricity usage grew by only 1%. Reasons for the decline in electric growth include increasing efficiency of appliances and other electrical equipment plus a shift toward less energy-intensive business activities.

Worldwide, electricity use continues to grow as well. In 2018, the world consumed over 23 trillion kWh, which was over two times the consumption in 1990. This growth is not expected to abate anytime soon.

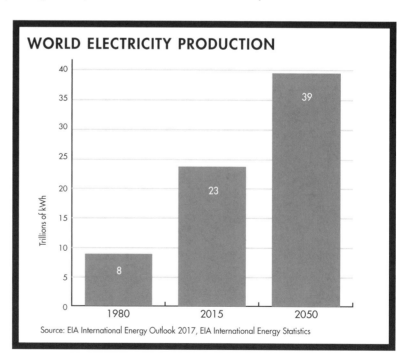

WORLD ELECTRICITY PRODUCTION

Trillions of kWh

1980: 8
2015: 23
2050: 39

Source: EIA International Energy Outlook 2017, EIA International Energy Statistics

Unbelievably, over a billion people currently lack access to grid electricity. If we assume globalization continues to bring affluence to developing regions, many of these will expect to share our modern standards of living and will soon contribute to even greater growth in world electric demand.

According to the U.S. Energy Information Administration (EIA), worldwide electricity production is projected to increase at an average annual rate of 1.5% between 2015 and 2050. While use in the industrialized world is expected to increase at a historically modest rate of 1% per year, use in the developing countries is expected to increase by 1.8% annually. By the year 2050, developing countries are expected to increase their percentage of world usage from today's 57% to 62%. And by 2050, world electricity output will have increased by 66% from the year 2015.

Of course, our hunger for electric power is not without significant cost. Consumers in the United States spent over $402 billion on electricity in 2018. The International Energy Agency has estimated that the world will need to spend more than $16 trillion over the next 20 years just to provide the necessary electric infrastructure that will accommodate growing demand. At the same time, electric generation — fueled worldwide by the burning of hydrocarbons — continues to negatively impact our natural environment. As we move into the 21st century, most observers now agree that mankind must develop new, more environmentally benign ways of generating and using electricity to create a sustainable future.

A Brief History of Electricity

The word electricity is derived from the Latin word *electricus*, which means to "produce from amber by friction." As long ago as 600 B.C., Greeks knew that amber could be charged by rubbing. And it was Thales of Miletus who many credit with the first discovery of electricity. He noticed that rubbing two pieces of amber together created a force that could attract light objects such as cat fur.

While man has long known that the phenomenon we now call electricity existed, it was not until much later that it was studied and ultimately put to use. In 1600, the English scientist William Gilbert described the electrification of many different substances and coined the word electricity. By 1660, scientists had invented a machine for producing static electricity by rotating and rubbing a ball of sulfur.

As society entered the 1700s, scientists began the work of harnessing electricity. In 1729, the conduction of electricity was discovered, and subsequent work identified substances that would act as conductors. And in 1745, the Leyden jar was invented.

This device contained a glass vial partially filled with water and a thick wire that could conduct an electrical charge. The Leyden jar was notable in that it was the first device that allowed electric charge to be stored and later discharged all at once (leading ultimately to the concept of electric current). It was also during this time that Benjamin Franklin invented the lightning rod, proving that lightning was actually a form of electricity.

In 1799, copper and zinc plates separated by cardboard soaked in salt water were used to create the first continuous and controlled source of electricity, the forerunner of our modern-day battery. Having a steady source of electricity pushed researchers' capabilities into a new realm, and by the mid-1800s we had laws that described the basic behavior of electricity (Ohm's law and Kirchoff's law) as well as various electric technologies such as the electromagnet, the electric motor, the electric generator, and electric arc lights. We also saw one of the first practical uses of electricity — the telegraph, invented by Samuel Morse around 1840.

As the world entered the industrial age, scientists and engineers pressed to create additional practical uses of electricity. The discovery of the self-excited dynamo — a generator that could quickly ramp up to full capacity — made it feasible to create small-scale generating stations, and by the mid-1870s electric arcs were lighting the streets of Paris, London, and New York. Arc lights, however, were too powerful for indoor uses, and widespread use of electricity awaited Thomas Edison's development of a practical incandescent bulb in 1879. Soon after this discovery, Edison patented his design for an electrical distribution system. On September 4, 1882, the Edison Electric Illuminating Company opened its first central generating station at Pearl Street in Manhattan, and the era of the electric utility was born. Soon thereafter, a number of small distribution systems were created and Benjamin Harrison, elected in 1888, became the first president to have electricity in the White House (although, as the story goes, he and his wife were afraid of being shocked by the light switches, so they opted to use the gas lights instead). Use of electricity to power street railways also became common, and by 1889 there were 154 of them in the U.S.

Broader development of electric utilities was hamstrung by the fact that initial systems were direct current (DC). DC systems at voltages safe for home use cannot efficiently distribute power for more than about a half mile due to losses of electricity along the distribution wires. At that time, raising voltages to transmit power and then lowering them again for household use was too expensive to be feasible. The breakthrough that led to today's modern utility came in 1888 when Nikola Tesla created workable alternating current (AC) generators and motors. Unlike DC power, AC power can be transmitted longer distances at low voltages without undue losses. Using Tesla's patents, George Westinghouse received a contract to construct a power plant at Niagara Falls. The plant opened in August 1895 and powered two 3.7 MW generators. Initially the power was used locally for the manufacture of aluminum and carborundum, but in 1896 a 20-mile transmission line was constructed to Buffalo where the power was used for lighting and street cars.

Soon the electrical giants Westinghouse and General Electric came to dominate electric power technology, and in the years between 1900 and the First World War new electrical appliances such as the refrigerator, washing machine, vacuum cleaner, and radiant heaters as well as improved light bulbs led to increasing demand for electricity. The concept of the vertically integrated utility that owned and operated electric generation, transmission, and distribution soon dominated the industry, leading to the need for regulation and, in some areas, municipalization of the utility function. Meanwhile, as part of the Depression-era New Deal, the federal government began construction of numerous federal hydro power projects.

Between 1945 and 1965 the utility industry continued to grow and investors became familiar with the steady, if unspectacular, returns provided by utilities. The technology for central generating units powered by coal, fuel oil, and natural gas matured, providing for increased efficiency and lower costs. Customers remained generally satisfied as technological innovations boosted transmission and distribution reliability at the same time that rates were falling.

The year 1965 marked the start of a new era. The Northeast blackout in November 1965 left over 30 million customers — including all of New York City — without power. This was perhaps our first realization that we had become dependent on an interconnected system that was less reliable than assumed. As we entered the 1970s, many utilities became enamored with the potential of nuclear energy, and construction began on a number of large nuclear generating units. Shocks soon to follow included the Arab Oil Embargo of 1973-1974, the Three Mile Island nuclear accident in March 1979, and subsequent rapidly increasing generation costs for many utilities. By the 1980s, many utilities were burdened with high debt levels and interest rates, incomplete power plant projects, slowing growth in the demand for electricity, the need for substantial electric rate increases, and increasing environmental concerns. Suddenly utilities found themselves portrayed in a negative light.

In the 1990s and 2000s, the turmoil continued. Encouraged by deregulation in the natural gas, airline, transportation, and some foreign electric industries, free market advocates began pushing for competition in the electric industry. This led to the breakup of vertically integrated utilities in some regions, the spectacular rise and fall of marketing companies such as Enron and Dynegy, financial difficulties driven by expansion of utilities into unregulated activities, and a U.S. marketplace split into varying market structures. Other regions of the world became equally fragmented, with some countries pushing competitive markets and others sticking with monopoly utilities.

In the mid-2010s, rapid industry evolution continued. Driven by technological and manufacturing advances, the cost of renewables fell significantly while wind and solar generation became the cheapest source of new generation in many regions of the world. The cost of batteries for grid storage also began dropping quickly. In some cases, combinations of renewable generation and batteries became competitive with the costs of operating existing nuclear or fossil fuel power plants. In the U.S., reductions in renewable costs combined with low natural gas costs resulted in a dramatic decrease in generation by coal and contributed to the closure of several nuclear power plants. Growth in distributed energy resources (DERs) including rooftop solar, combined heat and power (CHP), demand-side management (DSM), electric vehicles, behind-the-meter storage, and smart distribution systems resulted in utilities and their regulators rethinking traditional business models. And in most parts of the world, the industry acknowledged the need to transition away from fossil fuel generation in response to concerns about global climate change. Today it seems certain that the pace of change for the industry has accelerated and that energy companies will continue to rapidly evolve.

What you will learn:

- What electricity is

- What an electrical current is

- How electricity is created

- How electricity is used to perform useful tasks

- The physical delivery system

- Key physical properties of electricity

- The four key physical sectors of the electric business

2

2

SECTION TWO: WHAT IS ELECTRICITY?

Electricity is simply the flow of electrons through a conductor[1]. Electrons are the tiny negatively charged particles that are found in all atoms. Electricity is transmitted as loose electrons move from one atom to the next within a conductor. A conductor is any material that facilitates this transmittal of electricity.

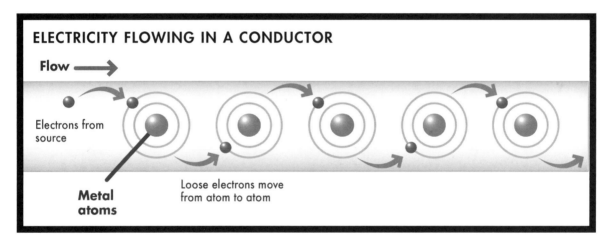

ELECTRICITY FLOWING IN A CONDUCTOR

Flow ⟶

Electrons from source

Metal atoms

Loose electrons move from atom to atom

Most practical applications of electricity require electrons to flow through a circuit. A circuit includes a source of electrons (a battery or generator), an energy-consuming device (such as a light bulb), and conductors (wire) that transmit the electrons to and from the bulb. In the simple circuit illustrated on page 12, the battery causes electrons to flow through the wire to the light bulb where light is created. The electrons then return to the battery via the wire and the electric circuit is complete. Note that the bulb does not "consume" the electrons, but rather the electrons flow through a material in the bulb causing it to glow.

Before we continue, there are several quantitative terms associated with the flow of electrons you will need to understand. The rate at which electrons flow through a conductor is called current and is measured by amperes or amps (A). If we were to compare the flow of electrons through a conductor to the flow of water through a hose,

---

[1]Throughout this book we will use the term electricity to mean the flow of electrons through a conductor, which is also known as current electricity. There is a second type of electricity known as static electricity. Static electricity is the transfer of electrons from one material to another and is not discussed in this book.

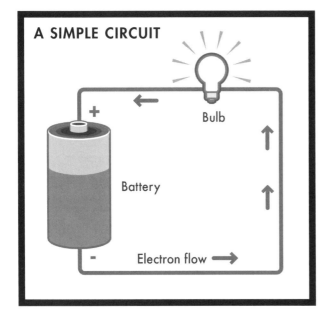

A SIMPLE CIRCUIT

Bulb

Battery

Electron flow →

this rate would be the equivalent of gallons per second. There are two factors that affect this rate — the force applied to the electrons and the resistance to flow within the conductor. The force that moves electrons is called voltage and is measured in volts (V). The higher the voltage, the faster the rate of flow (the higher the current). Voltage, then, is the equivalent of pressure in our hose. Resistance, which is measured in ohms (R), impedes the flow of electrons. As you might imagine, the higher the resistance in the conductor, the slower the rate of flow (the lower the current). Returning to our water analogy, ohms are equivalent to any friction or blockage that might slow down the flow of water through the hose. Current is always directly proportional to voltage and resistance as shown in a relationship known as Ohm's law:

$$\text{Current (amps)} = \frac{\text{Voltage (volts)}}{\text{Resistance (ohms)}}$$

SIX TYPES OF ENERGY

Electrical energy is one of six major types of energy:

Chemical energy — Stored energy released as the result of two or more atoms and/or molecules combining to form a chemical compound.

Electrical energy — Energy associated with the flow of electrons.

Electromagnetic energy — Energy associated with electromagnetic radiation including visible light, infrared light, ultraviolet light, x-rays, microwaves, radio waves, and gamma rays.

Mechanical energy — Energy that can be used to raise a weight.

Nuclear energy — Stored energy released as the result of particles interacting with or within an atomic nucleus.

Thermal energy — Energy associated with atomic and molecular vibrations that results in heat.

Electrical energy stands alone in value among the six because it can be easily transported and readily transformed into other useful energy forms: to mechanical energy via an electric motor; to electromagnetic energy via light bulbs, microwave ovens, etc.; and to thermal radiation via radiant heaters.

This means that you would maintain the same current in a circuit if you increased both the volts and the ohms by the same ratio. You would increase the current if you increased the voltage but did not change the ohms. Conversely, you would decrease the current if you left the voltage unchanged but increased the ohms.

Different voltages are used in a circuit depending on what is being done with the electricity. High voltages are used to transmit electricity long distances while lower voltages are used to power home appliances and office equipment. Voltages can be changed through the use of transformers. Transformers are able to change voltages because applying electricity to two different sized coils of wire in near proximity results in a voltage transformation. By adjusting the coil size, engineers can adjust voltage as required.

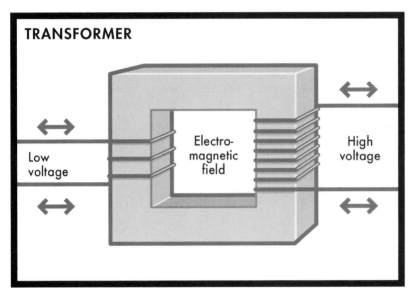

TRANSFORMER

Low voltage

Electro-magnetic field

High voltage

Most home appliances in the U.S. are operated on 110 V. Large appliances such as electric dryers and some electric ovens operate on a higher voltage of 220 V. We commonly refer to home electric services from the utility as 120/240 V services. Notice that while voltage may be supplied to a home at 120 V, the appliances use 110 V. The difference in voltage is due to resistance in home wiring. Standard residential voltages vary around the world, ranging from 100 V to 240 V. Commercial and industrial buildings often operate a number of their devices at higher voltages such as 480 V. The size of an electrical service is determined in amps. A typical home built today in the U.S. would have a service of 200 amps.

How Electricity Is Created

To begin the flow of electrons through a conductor, a source of energy is required. This can be either chemical or electromagnetic energy. Batteries and fuel cells operate by using chemical energy to free electrons from one material and transfer them to another via a conductor. Batteries and fuel cells contain three components — two electrodes and an electrolyte. The electrolyte reacts with the electrodes to create oxides that result in excess negative charge in one electrode (creating the negative terminal) and excess positive charge on the other (creating the positive terminal). The imbalance in charge creates an electric current when the terminals are connected to form a circuit.

Electromagnetic energy is used in two primary ways to create electricity. Solar or photovoltaic (PV) cells are made of materials that cause electrons to flow when light strikes the cell. As with a battery, the flow is directed through a circuit. The most common way of creating electricity — the electric generator — uses electromagnetic energy in a very different way. An electric generator creates electricity by what is called electromagnetic induction. Electromagnetic induction uses magnetism to make electrons flow. A source of mechanical energy (a steam turbine, gas turbine, wind turbine, or water

ELECTRICAL TERMINOLOGY

Current — The rate of flow of electrons.

Amps — The unit used to measure current.

Voltage — The force that moves electrons.

Volts — The unit used to measure voltage.

Kilovolts — Another unit used to measure voltage, equal to 1,000 volts.

Resistance — A measure of the strength of impedance, which is the physical property that slows down electrons.

Ohms — The unit used to measure resistance.

Transformer — A device used to change voltages in a circuit.

turbine) is used to spin a shaft connected to a coil. This coil is suspended between the poles of a magnet and is connected to wires in a circuit by metallic brushes. As the coil spins through the magnetic field, electrons flow through the coil and brushes and then into the electric circuit.

How Electricity Is Used to Perform Useful Tasks

You now know that electricity is the flow of electrons through a conductor. You also know that it flows through a conductor in a circuit under variable rates of flow. If that was all electricity did, however, it's unlikely you'd be reading about it in this book! What we've yet to discuss is that moving electrons create specific effects that can be harnessed to perform useful tasks. These effects include heat, light, and magnetism. To understand electricity it is important to remember that unlike natural gas, electrons are not consumed while creating value. They can, however, be directed through specific materials resulting in all kinds of useful by-products. For example, heat can be created by moving electrons through a wire made from a resistant material. The electric flow through the resistant material converts the electrical energy to heat energy, allowing consumers to heat their homes. Another use is to create light. LED bulbs are made out of semi-conductor material that emits light when an electric current flows

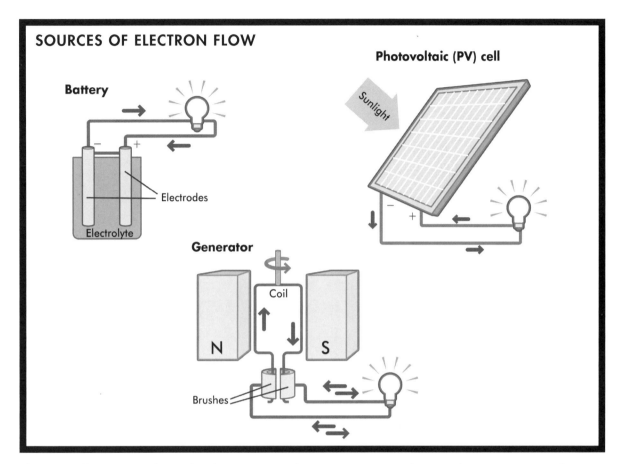

through the material. A third use comes from converting electrical energy to mechanical energy. Electromagnets are created when electric current flows through coils of conductive material. Electric motors harness these magnetic fields to spin a shaft, creating mechanical energy that can then be used in a variety of ways such as spinning a tool or powering an electric vehicle.

One additional way that electricity is used to create value involves the principle of control. By controlling the flow of electrons, electronic devices can be used to transfer information. This is the principle behind transistors and microchips, the two devices that have made modern technology possible[2]. For example, by controlling the flow in a specific way, we can represent the number 1 or 0, allowing us to digitize information.

The amount of electricity necessary to perform useful tasks is determined by the power required to move the electrons through a specific device. This power is measured in units called watts. A typical LED light bulb requires 8 watts to operate. Power used

---

[2] By far, the best explanation of how electrical devices work in plain language is a book found on many a child's bookshelf titled *The New Way Things Work*, by David Macaulay.

over time is commonly called energy. So anyone using that 8-watt bulb for one hour will consume 8 watt-hours of energy.

The current, voltage, and power available in a circuit are related:

Watts = Volts x Amps

So the power available in a home service of 200 A delivered at 120 V is:

Power (watts) = 120 V x 200 A = 24,000 W (which is the same as 24 kW)

As you have learned, electricity is delivered to the devices that use it via an electrical circuit. If a circuit is not complete, the flow of electrons will stop. Thus, in all circuits — including the electrical distribution system — electrons flow from one end of the source, through the conductor and devices, and then back to the source.

Now that you understand how current flows through a circuit, we need to confuse matters just a bit. Electric currents come in two types — direct current (DC) and alternating current (AC). In DC circuits the power flows continually in one direction, from the negative terminal to the positive terminal. In an AC circuit, the direction in which the electrons flow changes periodically and repeatedly. Electrons first flow from the generator toward the load. The flow then reverses direction and again flows to the load but from the opposite direction. Each time the direction of flow changes we say that the electricity has completed one-half cycle. A full cycle, then, is when the electricity flows first in one direction and then the opposite. The unit of hertz (Hz) is used to measure frequency, or how often electrons change direction. Utilities in most of the Americas and parts of Asia operate on a standard of 60 Hz (meaning that electrons complete 60 cycles per second). Elsewhere, a standard of

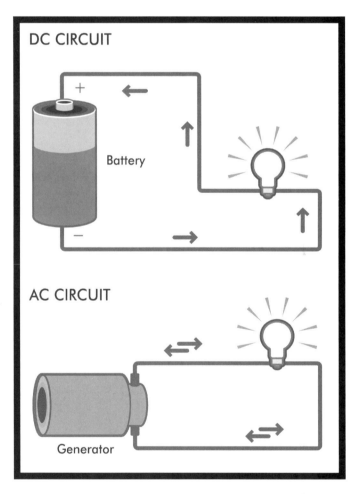

DC CIRCUIT

+

Battery

−

AC CIRCUIT

Generator

50 Hz is used, meaning that a hair dryer bought in the U.S. requires a converter for use in a London hotel.

The Key Components of the Electric Delivery System

Now let's take what you've learned about a simple circuit and expand it to explain how electricity is created and delivered to consumers. An electric delivery system is, in its basic sense, simply a very large circuit. The flow of electrons, or current, is created by the generator. The electrons are transmitted to and back from consumers via conductors — transmission and distribution lines. And completing the circuit are the millions of energy-consuming devices.

The voltage created by generators is generally several thousand volts. This voltage is then stepped up to transmission voltage by a step-up transformer. Banks of step-up transformers are typically located in a substation immediately adjacent to the generator. These transformers facilitate electric transmission because it is much more efficient

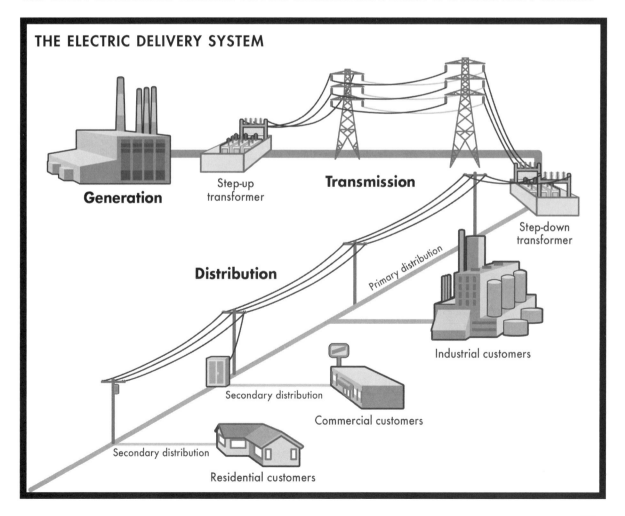

THE ELECTRIC DELIVERY SYSTEM

Generation

Step-up transformer

Transmission

Step-down transformer

Distribution

Primary distribution

Industrial customers

Secondary distribution

Commercial customers

Secondary distribution

Residential customers

to move electricity long distances at high voltages. Unfortunately, current at high voltages is capable of sparking or jumping large distances and is extremely dangerous to humans. This is why high voltage transmission lines are located on large towers.

As the electricity approaches an area where it will be consumed, the voltage is dropped to a safer voltage. This is performed by a distribution transformer located in a distribution substation. The electricity then continues its journey via the lower voltage distribution lines until it reaches the service line (the line entering a consumer's building). At the interconnection with the service line, the voltage is often transformed again to the necessary service voltage. The current then passes through the meter, flows through the consumer's internal wiring, through the consuming devices, and back through the system to the generator, completing the circuit.

In any electrical circuit, electrons always make their way back to the source generator. Thus, the electrons themselves are not used up. The reason that electrical systems require a continual input of energy (natural gas, coal, water flow, etc.) is simply to keep the electrons moving.

2   The Key Physical Properties of an Electric Delivery System

There are a number of physical properties unique to electricity that are extremely important to understand. As you will learn later in this book, electricity is a commodity like no other. Understanding these properties will help you to understand why the electricity business operates as it does.

Electricity Cannot Be Stored in Conductors

Flowing electrons cannot be stored in the conductors that transmit electricity from where it is produced to where it is consumed. This means the electrical system must be operated to ensure that supply and demand are continually in balance throughout the system at all times. If electrical supply is not available to match instantaneous electrical demand, the whole system will crash, resulting in blackouts. Thus an electrical system requires continual surveillance and adjustment to ensure supply always matches demand.

The Path of Electrical Flow Is Difficult to Control

Electrons flow on the path of least resistance. And if the least resistant path is from the transmission line through a wet tree branch to the ground, that's precisely where the electricity will flow. Similarly, if this is from one utility's transmission system into another interconnected utility's transmission system, that is where electrons will travel.

Thus all utilities on an interconnected system must cooperate in operating their systems as the action of one may cause electrons to flow into or out of the others' systems.

FOUR KEY PHYSICAL SECTORS

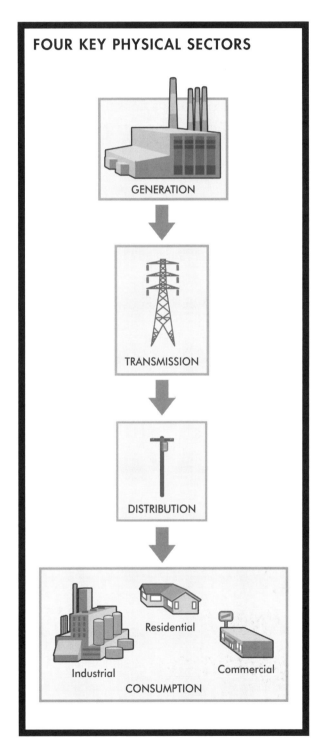

GENERATION

TRANSMISSION

DISTRIBUTION

Industrial   Residential   Commercial

CONSUMPTION

Disturbances Travel Very Quickly and Are Hard to Contain

Changes in voltage or frequency on electrical lines move at the speed of light, which is 984 million feet (300 million meters) per second. So any disturbance — say a sudden burst of high voltage or a frequency that is out of whack — also travels very quickly. This is why a tree hitting a power line in Oregon can quickly result (and has) in lights going out in Los Angeles. This means that not only must system operators cooperate, but they must also be prepared to react to one another's actions (and problems) almost instantly.

Outages and Significant Voltage or Frequency Fluctuations Are Not Acceptable

With the advent of modern electric controls and microchip-based devices, our consumption of electricity no longer tolerates momentary outages or fluctuations in voltage or frequency. Thus the entity that is responsible for matching supply and demand not only has to do so every minute of every day, but must also do it with little margin for error.

There you have it — the four physical properties of electricity that make it different from any other form of energy. These properties not only necessitate a centralized coordinating function called system operations, they also create business complexities unlike any other business in the world today.

The Four Key Physical Sectors of the Electricity Business

Now that we have studied how electricity is created and delivered, and discussed its key physical properties, we are ready to focus on the four key physical sectors of the electricity business. These are generation, transmission, distribution, and consumption. These are also the four components that comprise the circuit that we call the electric delivery system. Because generation, transmission, and distribution are designed to serve specific customer needs, we will discuss electric consumers first. This will be followed by a look at the generation, transmission, and distribution sectors. We will explore the business entities and market structures that provide these functions throughout much of the rest of this book.

2

why industrial customers can be served more cheaply, have more clout in the regulatory/political arena, and are generally more attractive customer targets for deregulated electric sales in states where such sales are allowed.

In looking at customer data it is important to remember that market characteristics vary regionally. For example, in Florida residential customers use over seven times as much electricity as industrial customers, while nationwide residential customers use only 1.5 times as much as industrial customers. As we will see later, the difference in usage patterns among the three customer classes creates significant differences in how the electrical system must be designed and operated to serve these customers.

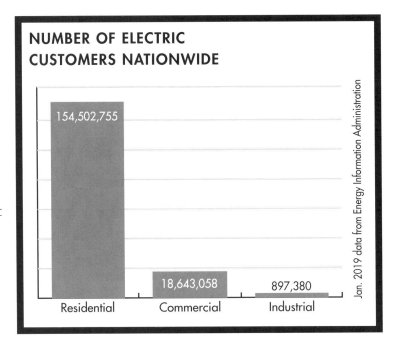

NUMBER OF ELECTRIC CUSTOMERS NATIONWIDE

154,502,755 — Residential
18,643,058 — Commercial
897,380 — Industrial

Jan. 2019 data from Energy Information Administration

Residential Customers

Over 154 million residential customers (including single-family homes and multi-family units) in the United States use electricity[1]. Residential electricity use accounts for approximately 39% of overall U.S. usage and has increased by an average of about 0.7% per year over the last 10 years. Consumption is expected to continue to grow minimally at a rate of about 0.4% per year between 2018 and 2050. Factors in the slow growth rate include ongoing improvements in the energy efficiency of building insulation, lighting, air conditioning, and other appliances. But a major shift to more energy-consuming devices such as electric vehicles could change this expectation quickly.

The top residential uses for electricity include space cooling, space heating, water heating, lighting, refrigeration, TVs, and clothes drying. Other devices that use significant quantities of electricity include freezers, stoves, personal computers, and furnace fans. Because of the significance of space cooling, residential usage is greatest in the summer and early fall months in most regions. During the spring and late fall, usage typically falls by as much as one-third. Winter usage is higher again due to increased

---

[1]Usage and price data in this section is taken from the EIA unless otherwise noted.

space heating and lighting demands. Usage in the coldest months of December and January is frequently as much as 80 to 90% of the peak summer usage.

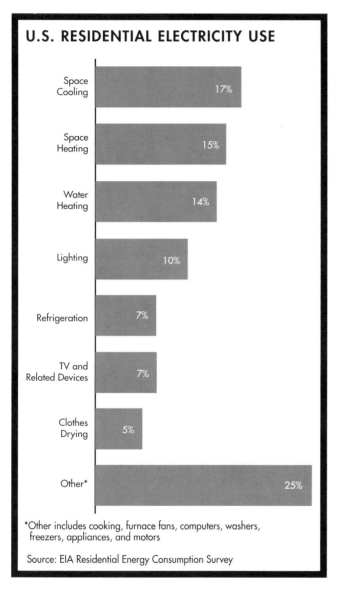

U.S. RESIDENTIAL ELECTRICITY USE

- Space Cooling: 17%
- Space Heating: 15%
- Water Heating: 14%
- Lighting: 10%
- Refrigeration: 7%
- TV and Related Devices: 7%
- Clothes Drying: 5%
- Other*: 25%

*Other includes cooking, furnace fans, computers, washers, freezers, appliances, and motors

Source: EIA Residential Energy Consumption Survey

Residential usage also changes significantly from hour to hour during the day. Usage is minimal during the late night and early morning hours, rises as residents get out of bed, falls again as residents go to school and work, and then climbs steadily from 3 p.m. through the evening. Often, peak usage late in a day will be more than double that in the middle of the night. Unlike residential consumption of other energy forms such as natural gas, electricity usage from year to year does not swing widely. In fact, over the last 10 years, U.S. residential energy usage has never varied from year to year by more than 6%.

Residential consumption patterns are rarely driven by price in the United States. In most areas, consumers are insulated from wholesale price swings by the nature of electric ratemaking, which often averages rates for periods of at least one year. This lack of demand response (to the real-time cost of electricity) has been a contributing factor to wholesale price spikes in competitive markets. In areas where residential consumers are exposed to market prices, demand response has been significantly greater.

Key residential customer needs and wants include:

- Reliability — Residential customers in the United States have come to expect that power will always be available when they need it. Since our society considers electricity a vital resource, even momentary outages are considered a significant nuisance and are generally unacceptable.

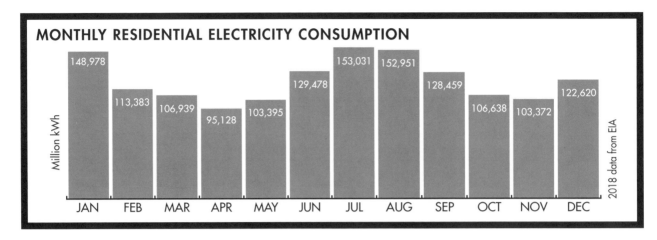

MONTHLY RESIDENTIAL ELECTRICITY CONSUMPTION

- Power quality to match needs of appliances — Not only do customers need high reliability (no outages), they also need electricity that fits within the voltage and frequency tolerances required by computers and the ever-increasing number of home appliances controlled by microchips. Not too many years ago, low voltages simply meant lights were dim. In today's world, low voltage means a number of devices will no longer work properly.

- Low prices — The cost of electricity is often a significant factor in consumers' budgets, especially among elderly and low-income customers who commonly have the least efficient homes and appliances.

- Stable prices — The reality of the electricity marketplace is that wholesale prices change hourly (and often within the hour). Almost all residential customers will say that they cannot deal with continually changing price levels. Even monthly price changes have proven to be highly unpopular in areas where introduction of regulatory reforms has resulted in monthly market price adjustments. Most residential customers prefer to lock in a specific price level for at least a year at a time.

- Energy efficiency — Many residential customers can significantly reduce electric consumption and costs through relatively simple energy efficiency measures. But most don't due to lack of knowledge or time. Services that make energy efficiency improvements more accessible have become important to many customers.

LOAD FACTOR

Load factor is a measure of how average usage relates to peak usage. Load factor is calculated as the total usage for a given period of time divided by what usage would have been had peak demand been maintained throughout the entire period. The following calculation measures load factor over the period of one year:

$$\text{Load factor} = \frac{\text{Actual annual usage (kWh)}}{\text{Peak demand (kW) x 8760 hours}}$$

Load factor is important since electrical services and generation must be designed to serve peak usage levels. During the hours when usage is less than peak, a portion of the facilities installed to meet peak loads sits idle.

- Energy choices — In recent years residential customers have begun to be aware of choices for electrical services. These include the option to buy green power from the grid, alternate rate schedules such as time-of-use, rooftop solar, various energy management services, and in some regions the choice of energy supplier and supply pricing alternatives. As these options become more widespread customer choice may become an increasingly important feature.

Residential customers typically pay more for electricity than other customer groups. There are three primary reasons for this. First, the distribution system required to serve residential customers is more expensive because services are delivered in small quantities and at lower voltages. Second, residential customers tend to have low load factors. Thus costs for residential customers are generally spread over fewer kilowatt-hours resulting in a greater per-kWh cost. And third, customer service costs are often much higher for residential customers since the utility is serving a large number of accounts, and residential customers are often less knowledgeable about their accounts than commercial or industrial customers. Residential customers in the U.S. paid an average rate of $0.129/kWh (compared to $0.107/kWh for commercial customers and $0.069/kWh for industrial customers) in 2018. It is important to note that rates vary significantly from state to state based on regulatory policies, the nature of the required transmission/distribution system, and the available resource base.

Commercial Customers

Over 18.5 million commercial customers use electricity in the U.S. Typical commercial customers include retail establishments, restaurants, motels and hotels, healthcare facilities, office buildings, and government agencies. Commercial customers are often distinguished from industrial customers by usage (a typical break point would be a peak demand of 500 or 1,000 kW, depending on the

AVERAGE RESIDENTIAL COSTS/kWh BY STATE

State	cents/kWh
Hawaii	32.5
Alaska	22.1
Massachusetts	21.6
Connecticut	21.2
Rhode Island	20.6
New Hampshire	19.6
California	18.9
New York	18.5
Vermont	18.0
Maine	16.1
Michigan	15.6
New Jersey	15.5
Wisconsin	14.4
Pennsylvania	13.9
Minnesota	13.4
Maryland	13.3
Kansas	13.1
District of Columbia	12.8
Arizona	12.8
New Mexico	12.7
Iowa	12.7
Delaware	12.6
Illinois	12.5
South Carolina	12.4
Ohio	12.4
Alabama	12.3
Colorado	12.1
Indiana	12.0
Nevada	11.9
Virginia	11.8
South Dakota	11.6
Florida	11.6
Georgia	11.4
Texas	11.4
Wyoming	11.4
North Carolina	11.3
West Virginia	11.3
Mississippi	11.2
Montana	11.2
Missouri	11.1
Oregon	10.9
Nebraska	10.8
Tennessee	10.7
Utah	10.5
Kentucky	10.4
North Dakota	10.3
Oklahoma	10.2
Idaho	10.2
Arkansas	9.8
Washington	9.6
Louisiana	9.3

2018 data from Energy Information Administration

utility). Commercial electricity use accounts for approximately 36% of overall U.S. usage and has increased on average by about 0.5% per year over the last 10 years. This increase in consumption is expected to continue at about 0.5% per year between 2018 and 2050, driven by small demand increases for computers and office equipment as well as growth of service businesses, but held down by increasing energy efficiency.

The top commercial uses for electricity include refrigeration, lighting, space cooling, ventilation, and computing. Other significant uses include space heating, water heating, and cooking. Because most commercial usage comes from businesses that run year round, it does not fluctuate nearly as much on a monthly basis as residential usage. In fact, usage during the lightest months (late winter and spring) is generally only 20% lower than peak months. Usage within the day also tends to fluctuate less than residential customers since many commercial facilities are used throughout the day and into the evening. Commercial electricity usage from year to year is relatively steady and in the last 10 years has varied by no more than 2%.

3

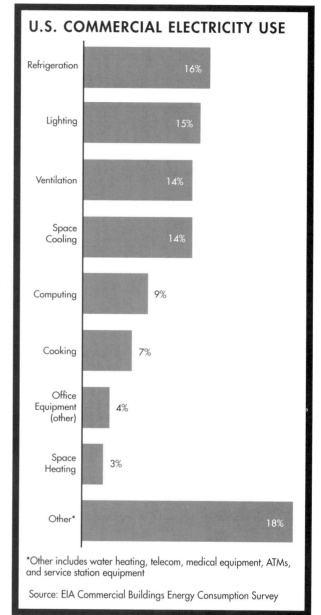

U.S. COMMERCIAL ELECTRICITY USE

Category	%
Refrigeration	16%
Lighting	15%
Ventilation	14%
Space Cooling	14%
Computing	9%
Cooking	7%
Office Equipment (other)	4%
Space Heating	3%
Other*	18%

*Other includes water heating, telecom, medical equipment, ATMs, and service station equipment

Source: EIA Commercial Buildings Energy Consumption Survey

Commercial customers are more likely to be price responsive than residential customers. In fact, many larger commercial customers are well-suited to alter demand when prices rise. Through use of various demand-shifting or energy efficiency measures, these businesses can reduce electricity consumption when it is cheaper to implement demand management measures than it is to buy electricity. And since it's simply an economic decision for most businesses, commercial customers tend to respond rapidly when proper incentives are in place.

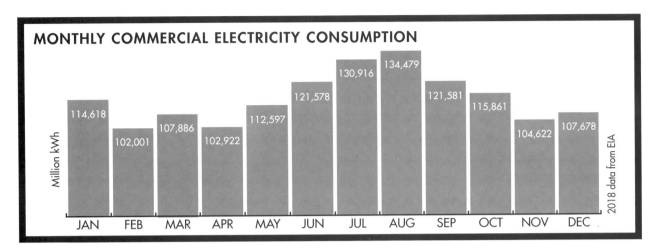

MONTHLY COMMERCIAL ELECTRICITY CONSUMPTION

Million kWh

JAN	FEB	MAR	APR	MAY	JUN	JUL	AUG	SEP	OCT	NOV	DEC
114,618	102,001	107,886	102,922	112,597	121,578	130,916	134,479	121,581	115,861	104,622	107,678

2018 data from EIA

Key commercial electric needs and wants include:

- Reliability — Commercial customers in the United States have come to expect that power will always be available when they need it. Virtually all commercial customers in the U.S. are unable to function without power. Even stores with natural lighting generally cannot operate their cash registers — and thus cannot serve customers — in the event of a power outage. Commercial customers with critical loads such as emergency lighting, food refrigeration, medical equipment, elevators, and telecom equipment often install their own back-up generators or batteries to maintain power should the utility service fail.

- Power quality to match needs of equipment — Not only do commercial customers require high reliability (no outages), they also place a high value on electricity that fits within the voltage and frequency tolerances applicable to computers and the ever-increasing loads of equipment controlled by microchips. In today's world, voltages or frequency fluctuations outside of tolerances can destroy sensitive equipment and bring businesses to a standstill. So even with high-quality power service, critical equipment such as computers, cash registers, and telecom is still often protected by power-conditioning devices that ensure uniform voltages and frequencies.

- Low prices — The cost of electricity is often a significant factor in commercial customers' cost of doing business. Thus they are often very attracted to ways to reduce their electricity costs.

- Stable prices and/or tools to manage electricity costs — The reality of the electricity marketplace is that wholesale prices change hourly (and often within the hour). Most commercial customers cannot effectively deal with continually changing price levels as they are more focused on running their businesses. The exception is larger commercial customers who can manage price exposure through technology. These more sophisticated customers are able to install demand management systems (for example, a smart building management system) that can automatically respond to price signals from the electricity provider.

- Energy efficiency — Many commercial customers pay close attention to energy usage and are willing to invest in energy efficiency measures if they are likely to result in rapid (one year or less) paybacks on investment.

Commercial customers typically pay considerably more for electricity than industrial customers but slightly less than residential customers. Commercial customers are frequently served at slightly higher voltages than residential customers (often 480 V instead of 120 V) and thus require less distribution facilities. This helps reduce distribution costs. They also tend to have higher load factors than residential customers, meaning that the ratio of peak use to average use is smaller, and peak-related costs can be spread over more kilowatt-hours. But customer service costs are still relatively high for commercial customers since the utility serves a large number of accounts, knowledge levels vary, and the customer group is highly diverse. Commercial customers in the U.S. paid an average rate of $0.107/kWh (compared to $0.129/kWh for residential customers and $0.069/kWh for industrial customers) in 2018. It is important to note that rates vary significantly from state to state based on regulatory policies, the nature of the required transmission/distribution system, and the available resource base.

Industrial Customers

Almost 900,000 industrial customers use electricity in the U.S. But don't let this small number fool you — the importance of this sector belies its small number of accounts. While comprising about one-half of one percent of customers in the U.S., industrial customers consume over 25% of U.S. electrical production.

Typical industrial customers include manufacturing, construction, mining, agriculture, fishing, forestry, electronics, and food processing. Large industrial users of electricity

AVERAGE COMMERCIAL COSTS/kWh BY STATE

State	cents/kWh
Hawaii	30.0
Alaska	19.0
Connecticut	16.8
Massachusetts	16.8
Rhode Island	16.5
California	16.5
New Hampshire	15.8
Vermont	15.2
New York	14.5
Maine	12.4
New Jersey	12.2
District of Columbia	12.0
Alabama	11.3
Michigan	11.2
Wisconsin	10.9
Arizona	10.7
Mississippi	10.5
Minnesota	10.5
Kansas	10.4
Maryland	10.4
Tennessee	10.4
Indiana	10.4
South Carolina	10.2
Montana	10.2
New Mexico	10.2
Colorado	10.1
Ohio	9.9
Iowa	9.8
Delaware	9.7
Georgia	9.7
Wyoming	9.6
Kentucky	9.6
South Dakota	9.5
Florida	9.4
West Virginia	9.3
Missouri	9.2
North Dakota	9.1
Illinois	9.0
Pennsylvania	8.9
Nebraska	8.9
Oregon	8.9
Louisiana	8.7
Washington	8.7
North Carolina	8.7
Virginia	8.4
Utah	8.4
Texas	8.1
Idaho	7.9
Oklahoma	7.9
Nevada	7.9
Arkansas	7.7

2018 data from Energy Information Administration

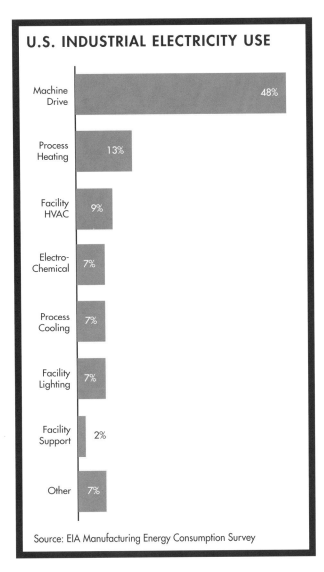

U.S. INDUSTRIAL ELECTRICITY USE

Machine Drive — 48%
Process Heating — 13%
Facility HVAC — 9%
Electro-Chemical — 7%
Process Cooling — 7%
Facility Lighting — 7%
Facility Support — 2%
Other — 7%

Source: EIA Manufacturing Energy Consumption Survey

include aluminum, chemicals, cement, forest products, glass, metal casting, petroleum refining, pulp and paper, and steel. As discussed earlier, some utilities use usage levels to classify industrial customers rather than attempting to evaluate end user types. A typical break point between commercial and industrial would be 500 or 1,000 kW of peak demand. Industrial electricity use in the U.S. has increased over the last 10 years by about 0.6% per year. This increase in consumption is expected to continue at an annual rate of about 0.9% over the next 25 years driven by industrial growth due to low fuel prices and electrification of some industrial end uses.

Industrial uses for electricity are dominated by machine drive, with other significant uses including process heating, HVAC (heating, ventilating, and air conditioning), electro-chemical processes, process cooling, and lighting. Because much of industrial usage is for manufacturing that runs year round, usage does not fluctuate considerably from month to month. In fact, usage during the lightest months (mid-winter) is generally only 10% lower than peak months. Usage across the day does not vary as widely as other customer groups since many industrial facilities operate around the clock. Industrial electricity usage from year to year swings much more widely than the other sectors due to business cycles. Over the last 10 years, U.S. industrial energy usage has experienced occasional sharp fluctuations with a 5.9% increase in 2010 and a 3.2% decline in 2018.

Industrial customers are more likely to be price responsive than any other customer group as electric consumption is often a significant factor in their cost of doing business. These customers are also much more likely to have alternatives than other customer groups. If electricity rates get too high, manufacturing might be moved to other lower-cost states or even other countries. And some customers have the option to generate their own electricity when it's cost-effective. Many industrial customers are also

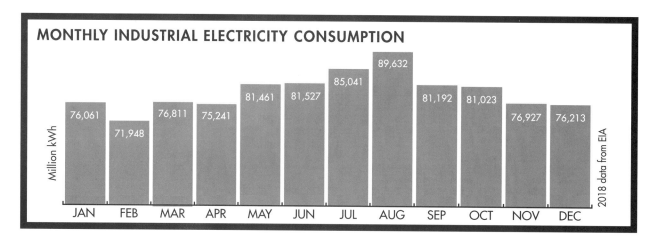

well-suited to price-responsive actions with their demands. Demand can often be shifted to lower price periods, energy efficiency measures can significantly reduce electricity consumption, and many industrial customers can handle periodic interruption of power allowing them to take advantage of cheaper interruptible rate schedules. Industrial customers commonly have the internal expertise and capital to evaluate and implement cost-saving options and/or are able to afford outside energy expertise.

Key industrial customer electric needs and wants include:

- Reliability — Unexpected loss of power can cause costly problems for industrial customers. Because large manufacturing facilities are expensive to build and maintain, industrial customers lose profits whenever their facilities are idle. Many industrial customers back-up critical loads with back-up generators or uninterruptible power supply (UPS) systems. In some cases, industrial customers use their generators to supply some or all of their power needs on site. This insulates them from concerns about utility power reliability.

- Power quality to match needs of equipment — Virtually all industrial processes are now run by electronic control systems. These systems tend to be highly sensitive and can be shut down or even damaged by voltage and frequency fluctuations or spikes. And as we've already seen, unexpected shutdowns can be costly.

- Low prices — The cost of electricity is often a significant factor in industrial customers' cost of doing business. Thus industrial customers have strong incentives to continually find ways to reduce their electricity costs.

- Stable prices — Industrial customers are much more likely to have their electricity prices tied to wholesale market conditions. This is because their large usage more closely resembles a wholesale customer than a retail customer. Some customers can handle the wholesale price fluctuations, others cannot. Large industrial customers are much more likely to take advantage of financial instruments to manage price risk if they cannot get price certainty from their utility or marketer.

- Tools to manage energy costs — Many industrial customers pay prices for electricity that vary from hour to hour. Rates may be significantly higher (as much as 100% higher) during peak hours than off-peak hours. Thus industrial customers need real-time information on energy usage and control systems or other technology that allows them to manage their overall energy use during higher-priced periods.

- Energy efficiency — Since industrial customers are huge consumers of electricity (an annual bill of $1 million is not uncommon), small percentage savings in electricity can add up to significant dollars. So industrial customers are continually looking for new ways to boost the efficiency of their electricity use.

- Timely and accurate billing — Because most industrial customers now use sophisticated cost management systems, timely and accurate billing information of their electricity use is very important to their ability to manage their businesses.

- Alternatives for bilateral contracts — Many larger companies are looking for contractual alternatives to utility supply. These may include the opportunity for longer-term price certainty or other options such as long-term renewable energy contracts. In states without direct access, large customers sometimes work with their utility to develop negotiated utility supply contracts or methods for the customer to achieve a "virtual" bilateral contract with a third-party supplier.

AVERAGE INDUSTRIAL COSTS/kWH BY STATE	
State	cents/kWh
Hawaii	26.1
Alaska	17.3
Rhode Island	15.4
Massachusetts	14.5
Connecticut	13.9
California	13.4
New Hampshire	13.1
Vermont	10.6
New Jersey	10.1
Maine	9.1
North Dakota	8.5
District of Columbia	8.3
Maryland	8.2
Minnesota	7.8
South Dakota	7.8
Florida	7.8
Delaware	7.7
Wisconsin	7.7
Nebraska	7.5
Kansas	7.5
Michigan	7.3
Colorado	7.3
Indiana	7.2
Missouri	7.0
Virginia	6.9
Pennsylvania	6.8
Wyoming	6.7
Ohio	6.7
Illinois	6.7
Arizona	6.6
Iowa	6.6
Idaho	6.5
West Virginia	6.4
North Carolina	6.2
Oregon	6.2
South Carolina	6.2
Mississippi	6.1
Nevada	6.1
Alabama	6.1
New York	6.0
Utah	5.9
Georgia	5.8
Tennessee	5.7
New Mexico	5.7
Texas	5.5
Kentucky	5.5
Arkansas	5.5
Louisiana	5.3
Montana	5.3
Oklahoma	5.2
Washington	4.7

2018 data from Energy Information Administration

Industrial customers typically pay significantly less for electricity than other consumers. Industrial customers are frequently served at high voltages (anywhere from 2.4 kV to as high as 60 kV) and thus require less distribution facilities, which reduces distribution costs. Industrial customers also tend to have high load factors, so peak-related costs can be spread over more kilowatt-hours. Customer service costs are relatively low since there are fewer customers and they are more likely to be knowledgeable about their electricity use. Industrial customers in the U.S. paid an average rate of $0.069/kWh (compared to $0.129/kWh for residential customers and $0.107/kWh for commercial customers) in 2018. Again, it is important to note that rates vary significantly from state to state based on regulatory policies, the nature of the required transmission/distribution system, and the available resource base.

Aggregate Demand Curves

Because electricity cannot be stored in transmission or distribution wires, electric providers must be prepared to service the total demand from their customers at all moments during the day. This is true for utilities in regulated states that must plan to have enough generation available to serve their customers; it is true for Independent System Operators (ISOs) that must plan to have enough generation available to serve the entire marketplace; and it is true for retail marketers that must plan enough supply to match their contracted customers' demand as closely as possible or risk significant financial exposure for balancing costs. Thus it is important to understand aggregate customer behaviors. Unlike the gas business, where transactions tend to take place on a daily basis, electricity sales and price fluctuations often occur in increments of one hour, and for balancing power, in increments as short as five minutes. So hourly and even intra-hourly usage fluctuations are important to clearly understand.

A typical hourly load curve might look like this:

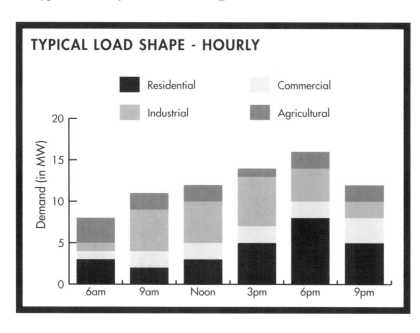

Observe the change across the day for the various customer classes. The agricultural sector peaks in the early morning because farmers do their water pumping before the heat of the day. Residential usage climbs in the morning as residents wake up, falls as they go to work and school, and then climbs through the afternoon and early evening as they return home. Commercial and industrial uses are steadier during the day but fall significantly at night as many businesses close.

Seasonal patterns are also important since some customers' electricity consumption varies greatly by season. The annual seasonal load curve for the U.S. looks like this:

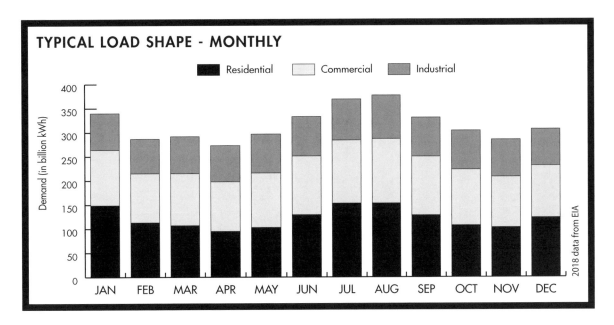

As mentioned earlier, customer mixes and weather patterns vary significantly by region. And as more customers invest in distributed resources such as rooftop solar, storage, flexible loads, and electric vehicles, load patterns in some regions may begin to change from traditional patterns. Since electric markets are constrained to regional areas by the lack of transmission, it is critical that industry players understand the consumption patterns of each region in which they are active.

What you will learn:

- What generation is

- The different types of electric generation

- The characteristics of each generation type

- The costs associated with each generation type

- Environmental concerns with each generation type

- How demand response serves as an alternative to generation

- How different generation sources are used to meet the demand curve

- Who owns generation

- How utilities and generation companies evaluate needs and develop generation portfolios

- Future generation sources

4

SECTION FOUR: GENERATION

Now that you have a general understanding of the needs of various electric customers, it's time to turn our attention to the physical system that is designed to deliver service to them. We will begin with a discussion of generation, which is the creation of flowing electrons. In later sections we will consider the other key components of the delivery system — transmission, distribution, and system operations.

Generation fuel sources are quite diverse and include coal, nuclear, natural gas, petroleum, hydro, and various forms of renewable energy. Within any of these fuel sources, the technology employed to generate electricity can be diverse as well (for instance, gas technology includes steam turbines, combined-cycle turbines, reciprocating engines, and single-cycle combustion turbines). Each type of generation has unique operating and cost characteristics that make it more or less suitable to a specific supply need. This is why utilities or generating companies generally build generation portfolios comprising varied generation types. These can then be used to match the needs of their customers as well as the specific needs of their geographic location.

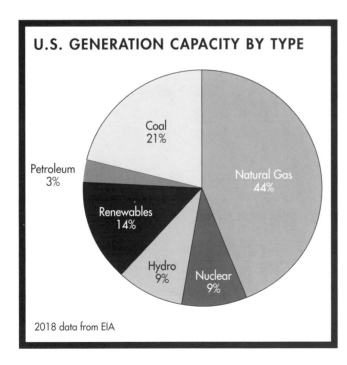

U.S. GENERATION CAPACITY BY TYPE

Coal 21%

Petroleum 3%

Renewables 14%

Hydro 9%

Nuclear 9%

Natural Gas 44%

2018 data from EIA

U.S. summer generation capacity is approximately 1,150,000 MW. The United States' generation portfolio that provides this capacity comprises many types of power plants with natural gas plants having the largest total capacity. But because some units are run more frequently than other types of generation, the generation output percentages look significantly different as you can see in the chart on page 38. Note that natural gas and coal are the top sources for 2018, followed by nuclear, renewables, hydro, and petroleum. These percentages vary from year to year

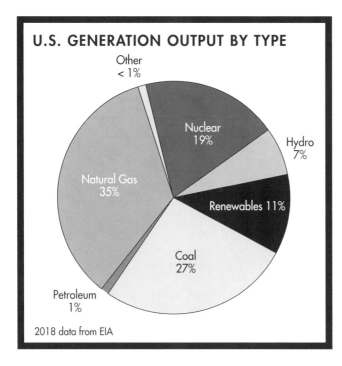

U.S. GENERATION OUTPUT BY TYPE

Other < 1%
Nuclear 19%
Hydro 7%
Natural Gas 35%
Renewables 11%
Coal 27%
Petroleum 1%

2018 data from EIA

based on factors such as the cost of natural gas and coal, the amount of hydro power available due to weather conditions, the growth of renewables, plant retirements, and the total amount of consumption.

U.S. generation capacity grew by an annual average of 1.2% for the 10 years from 2008 to 2018. The majority of this growth was due to construction of natural gas units and renewable projects, while a number of coal units were retired. As of 2019, the majority of planned new generation in the U.S. is natural gas, wind, and solar. Also expected to come online in the next five years are two new nuclear units. Coal capacity will continue to decline with over 75 units planned for retirement between 2018 and 2022.

4

Changing Generation Output over Time

As market, technology, and regulatory conditions change over time, the types of generation used evolve as well. In the current decade, we are experiencing an unprecedented shift in generation output from coal to natural gas and renewables. Until recently, coal had been the largest source of electricity generation in the United States since the mid-1900s. But in 2016 natural gas supplanted coal as the largest source, and in the month of April 2019, renewables also generated more electricity than coal plants. It is likely that renewable output will eventually surpass natural gas output, though that is still a number of years into the future.

Types of Generation

Utilities or generating companies try to match generation types with the aggregate needs of their customers. To understand how this is done, it is important to first understand that each generation type has unique operating, financial, and environmental characteristics. Key characteristics include capital costs, variable costs, operational flexibility, environmental impacts, fuel availability, and restraints on locations

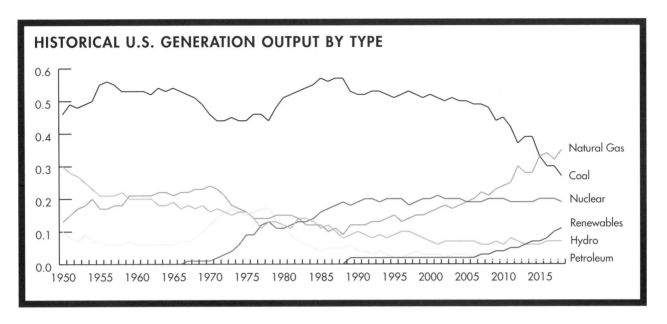

HISTORICAL U.S. GENERATION OUTPUT BY TYPE

where units can be constructed. Following is a discussion of each generation type and an assessment of the key characteristics outlined above. It is important that you clearly understand these fundamental characteristics as they will dictate which units run when and the generation type and technology used in the construction of new plants.

Coal

The ready availability of low-cost coal historically made coal-fired generation a favorite of many U.S. utilities. Most coal-fired generation employs steam turbine technology where coal is burned to heat water in boiler tubes. The water becomes steam and is run through a steam turbine that drives a generator shaft to create electricity. Because of economies of scale, most coal units are fairly large — in the range of 250 to 1,500 MW. The capital costs associated with building coal units are generally high compared with gas units, but many existing units have been online for a number of years and thus have been significantly depreciated. Operations and maintenance (O&M) costs are relatively low depending on the age of the unit. Fuel costs historically tended to be among the lowest of generation sources in the U.S. Due to technological constraints, coal units have limited operational flexibility. If the unit is running at partial power it can often be ramped up or down in response to system needs. But if the boiler has gone cold, it will require several hours to get to full operation. Because burning coal is responsible for considerable emissions (including CO_2, NO_x, SO_2, mercury, and particulates) coal units have a higher environmental impact than other sources of generation. For this reason and because of high transportation costs, there are areas of the country that do not use much coal to generate electricity. Other areas have historically been highly dependent on coal generation.

Beginning in the mid-2000s a number of utilities and merchant generators planned for construction of new coal units. But rising construction costs, falling natural gas prices, and opposition due to concerns over emissions led to cancellation or postponement of many projects. By the 2010s, coal had fallen out of favor due to declining costs for natural gas and renewable generation and increasing concerns about environmental impacts. Numerous existing coal units were retired and virtually all planned new projects were cancelled. Some companies began to consider cleaner Integrated Gasification Combined Cycle (IGCC) units, and two new units were completed in the U.S. But high costs and operational barriers for these newer technologies have slowed further development. Meanwhile ongoing falling costs for renewable and natural gas generation led many in the industry to predict that in the next few decades we will see the end of all coal generation in the U.S.

GENERATION CHARACTERISTICS

Capital cost — The up-front costs associated with buying equipment and constructing the generation unit, expressed in $/MW capacity.

Variable cost — The costs associated with running a generation unit that are directly related to the unit output, including fuel, water, and maintenance. These costs are expressed in $/MWh.

Operational flexibility — How quickly can a unit be turned on or off, and how quickly can it ramp from low power to full power?

Time to permit and construct — How long it takes to permit and build a new unit.

Environmental impact — What environmental impacts result from construction and operation, and what is the cost of environmental mitigation?

Fuel availability — How certain is future fuel supply?

Location — Can the unit be located near loads or is it located remote from loads thus requiring transmission investment?

Controllability — Can the output of a unit be dispatched by an operator to a specific output level or is output determined by factors such as wind, sunshine, or water flow? And if the unit is not dispatchable, how variable is the output of the unit?

Nuclear

A number of nuclear units were brought online in the United States in the 1970s and 1980s. These units are generally large and range in size from 600 to over 1,200 MW. Nuclear generation uses the heat of nuclear fission to create steam that is then run through a steam turbine. Capital costs associated with new nuclear units are very high, but as the units age and are depreciated their book values have declined. Variable costs including fuel are generally low, but fixed maintenance costs are high due to the extreme safety procedures required as well

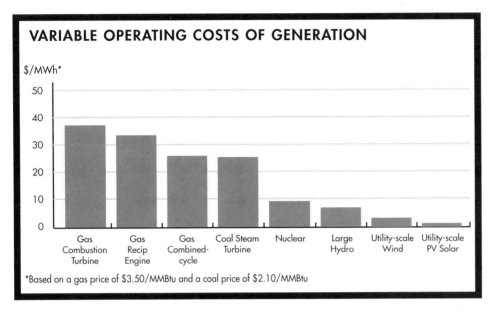

VARIABLE OPERATING COSTS OF GENERATION

$/MWh*

*Based on a gas price of $3.50/MMBtu and a coal price of $2.10/MMBtu

as the need to collect for future decommissioning costs. Because of the technology employed, nuclear units do not have good operational flexibility, and start-up times are usually measured in days. Because of this inflexibility, nuclear units are used for baseload needs. New development of nuclear generation in the U.S. has been hampered by key issues — the lack of a waste disposal site for spent fuel, public concerns over the risks of a major nuclear accident or terrorist attack, and high costs.

Public concerns about nuclear power risks were increased by the crisis in Fukushima, Japan, where the March 11, 2011, earthquake and tsunami caused severe damage to nuclear reactors owned by Tokyo Electric Power Company. The effects of the natural disaster damaged the power plants, disabling primary and backup power systems and resulting in core meltdowns, radiation releases, and the need to evacuate over 100,000 people from their homes. Although no deaths occurred directly related to the radiation release, long-term health effects are unknown. The units affected were permanently damaged and have been shut down. Some countries such as Germany responded by announcing plans to eliminate all nuclear power over time. Others such as the U.S. adjusted safety contingencies based on what was learned from Fukushima and continued moving forward with existing plans.

Despite the perceived safety issues, nuclear generation is favorable from the standpoint of emissions — no greenhouse gases or pollutants such as NO_x, SO_2, or mercury are emitted from nuclear generation. The first new nuclear unit in the U.S. since 1996 was brought into commercial operation in 2016, and as of 2019 two more new units are under construction and expected to be online later in the decade. A partially constructed two-unit project in South Carolina was cancelled in 2017 due to high costs and construction issues, and no further new units (beyond the two under construction) are currently forecast. Meanwhile, a number of older nuclear units are being retired, resulting in an expected overall decrease in U.S. nuclear capacity. But elsewhere, in countries such as China, India, Korea, Russia, and the United Arab Emirates construction of new nuclear units continues.

Natural Gas

Much of the new generation in recent years is natural gas-fueled. Gas-fired generation makes use of four primary technologies — combustion turbines that use natural gas directly to fire a turbine that drives the generator shaft; steam turbines that burn natural gas to create steam in a boiler that is then run through a steam turbine; combined-cycle units that utilize a combustion turbine (fired by natural gas) and then a steam turbine (wherein waste heat from the combustion turbine is used to produce steam that is then run through the steam turbine); and reciprocating internal combustion engines that use the motion of pistons to convert heat energy to mechanical energy that drives a generator. Utility-owned natural gas units vary significantly in size, ranging from as small as 1 MW to over 500 MW. Natural gas is also used to fuel on-site cogeneration units and backup generators for many buildings. Capital costs associated with natural gas units are considerably lower than other generation sources. O&M costs are also generally low. Fuel costs vary depending on the market value of natural gas. As you might imagine, a major concern among owners of natural gas generation are the historic fluctuations in natural gas prices. Depending on technology, natural gas units can be very flexible operationally. Combustion turbines and recipro-

---

WILL CHEAP GAS LAST IN THE U.S.?

The use of natural gas for generation in the U.S. has been boosted by various factors. One is that natural gas combusts more cleanly than other fossil fuels meaning that emissions are significantly lower per MWh of output. A second is that advancements in combined-cycle generation technology have greatly increased the efficiency of gas generation. The last factor has been the drop in natural gas costs in the U.S. that began in 2008 due to development of new unconventional natural gas resources such as shale gas. A key concern over too much dependence on natural gas generation is that historically natural gas prices have been volatile. Natural gas generation looks very good when prices fall below $4/MMBtu, but when prices hit $12/MMBtu it seems very expensive! Henry Hub (which is the most common U.S. natural gas reference point) daily prices have fluctuated from a low of $1.77/MMBtu to a high of $11.98/MMBtu over the last 15 years. Despite this volatility, prices in recent years have been near or below $3/MMBtu.

Should supply planners assume that today's low prices will persist? Through new drilling techniques, gas producers have recently accessed huge new supplies that were previously unavailable, and many analysts believe that economic U.S. gas reserves have expanded many-fold. Current estimates suggest that we may have close to 100 years' worth of natural gas reserves. And as of 2019, the EIA forecasts Henry Hub prices below $5/MMBtu through 2050. History tells us that natural gas prices rise and fall periodically, and only the future will tell if this cycle is destined to repeat or low prices will continue.

cating engines, often called peakers, can be started and stopped within minutes. Combined-cycle turbines take a bit longer to start, but can reach full power within an hour. Combustion turbines, reciprocating engines, and combined-cycle turbines can be flexibly ramped once under operation. Steam turbines may require up to six hours to go from cold status to full power but have reasonable ramp flexibility. Gas units do have air quality impacts as emissions include CO_2 and NO_x. Emissions are less than from other fossil fuel power generation such as coal and petroleum, so

---

HEAT RATE

The heat rate of a generating unit is a means of measuring the efficiency of the unit by answering the question "How much fuel is required to generate a kWh of electricity?" Other factors being equal, a smaller heat rate is better, since this means less fuel is being consumed to create a unit of electricity. Typical heat rates for various generation types are as follows:

Unit Type	Typical Heat Rate (Btu/kWh)
Natural gas steam turbine	10,000 — 12,000
Natural gas combined-cycle	6,200 — 8,000
Natural gas combustion turbine	8,000 — 10,000
Natural gas reciprocating engine	7,500 — 8,500
Coal steam turbine	9,000 — 11,000
Natural gas turbine with cogeneration	5,000 — 6,500

The variable fuel cost of operating a unit can be determined by multiplying the cost of fuel by the heat rate (and usually making some unit conversions). For instance, a natural gas combined-cycle unit with a gas cost of $4/MMBtu and a heat rate of 7,000 Btu/kWh will have a fuel cost of $28/MWh.

---

in regions where new gas units replace these types of power, gas generation is often considered favorable from an environmental standpoint. But in regions where gas competes with renewable generation, it can be considered an environmental detriment.

Hydro

Hydro power is the backbone of many electric generation systems across the United States where significant hydro resources are available (notably the West and parts of the Southeast). Hydro power is created by running water from a reservoir or flowing river through a hydraulic turbine that spins and drives a generator shaft. For units with upstream water storage in a reservoir or holding pond, the power output can be controlled by simply adjusting the water flow, resulting in units with flexible output. Hydro units range from very small (100 kW) to very large (over 500 MW) with many units in the 100 MW range. Most hydro units were built a number of years ago (with some units dating back to the 1920s), so capital costs have generally been depreciated. O&M costs are generally low and, of course, there is no fuel cost once water rights are acquired. Given their operational flexibility, many hydro units are useful for managing peak loads and for power regulation purposes (keeping supply and demand in balance minute by minute) as well as for restoring the grid after a blackout. Although a new hydro dam would now be considered to have large environmental impacts, existing units are generally considered environmentally favorable, with the exception of impacts on fish populations and

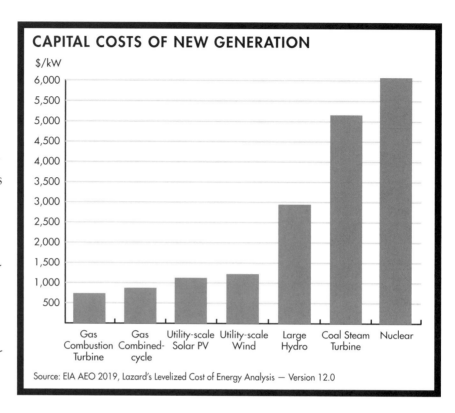

CAPITAL COSTS OF NEW GENERATION

Source: EIA AEO 2019, Lazard's Levelized Cost of Energy Analysis — Version 12.0

downstream activities. A related technology is pumped hydro storage, which uses off-peak power to pump water uphill into a reservoir, thus making it available for generation during peak hours. This process is used by utilities as a form of electricity storage.

Petroleum

A limited number of utilities make use of petroleum generation as an alternative to natural gas. Petroleum generation is typically seen in regions where natural gas supply is limited or where utilities utilize fuel-switching units with onsite petroleum tanks to provide backup in the event gas supply is unavailable or prohibitively expensive. The technology used in petroleum generation is similar to natural gas with a few changes to account for physical characteristics of the different fuel. Thus operational characteristics of petroleum units are similar to natural gas units. The major drawbacks to petroleum units are that fuel is often significantly more expensive and environmental impacts are greater than their natural gas counterparts. In fact, some areas of the country do not permit petroleum generation due to air quality concerns.

Renewables

Renewable electricity generation is a broad category fueled by sources that can be naturally replenished. These include geothermal, solar, wind, biomass, municipal solid

RENEWABLE ENERGY

Renewable electricity generation is fueled by sources that can be naturally replenished. These include:

Biomass — Organic non-fossil fuel that is burned directly to create steam for a steam turbine, or biogas used in a gas turbine. Biogas is created by decomposition of organic material at landfill or agricultural sites and is often at least 50% methane.

Geothermal — Hot water or steam extracted from underground reservoirs in the earth's crust that is used to drive steam turbines.

Hydro — Small-scale hydro generation, often run-of-the-river (meaning no reservoir is created), and usually less than 30 MW in size.

Municipal Solid Waste (MSW) — Garbage incinerated in a furnace or fluidized bed combustor to create heat and then steam to drive a steam turbine.

Solar — Sunlight applied to a photovoltaic cell (a substance that directly converts light energy to electricity) or sunlight used to heat liquids to create steam that is then used in a steam turbine.

Wave — Electric generator driven by the movement of ocean water.

Wind — Electric generator whose shaft is driven by the force of wind across a wind turbine.

waste, and smaller-scale hydro generation (usually less than 30 MW). Technologies used vary widely, and the size of renewable units tends to be small. Capital costs per unit vary greatly. Wind and utility-scale solar PV projects are often cost-competitive with other generation alternatives on a 10-year overall cost basis. O&M costs vary greatly by technology as well. The two big advantages of renewable power are that many technologies have no ongoing fuel cost (wind, solar) and environmental impacts are generally minimal. One drawback is that many renewable sources are variable and not always available. Thus system operators must plan for other flexible resources when including renewables in the generation mix.

Development of renewable generation — especially wind and solar power — has accelerated in recent years. Factors foster-

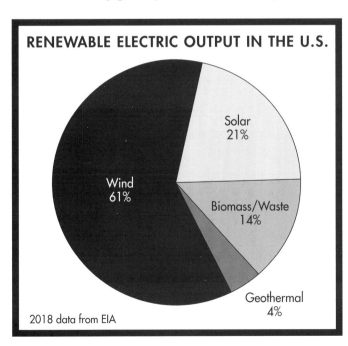

RENEWABLE ELECTRIC OUTPUT IN THE U.S.

Solar 21%

Wind 61%

Biomass/Waste 14%

Geothermal 4%

2018 data from EIA

(RPS) that require utilities and/or retail marketers to acquire a certain percentage of their generation portfolio from renewable resources. Many utilities and generating companies favor new construction of renewable or gas-fired units in part due to the relative ease in obtaining environmental permits. At the same time many older coal units are being retired in part due to new more stringent environmental rules.

ENVIRONMENTAL ISSUES BY GENERATION TYPE	
Generation Type	**Environmental Issues**
Coal	• CO_2 • NO_x • SO_2 • Mercury • Other heavy metal particulates • Land use disruption for mining • Use of diesel locomotives to transport coal
Nuclear	• Low-level radiation release through mining and waste • Potential for high-level radiation release in an accident
Natural Gas	• NO_x • CO_2 • Land use disruption for drilling
Hydro	• Impact on downstream fish and other species
Renewables	• Land use disruption for wind, solar, and biomass

Electric Generation, Global Warming, and Greenhouse Gas Regulation

A majority of the world's scientific community and most of the world's political community now agree that man's activities in burning carbon-based fuels (coal, petroleum, and natural gas) are resulting in raised concentrations of greenhouse gases that increase the earth's average temperature and destabilize weather patterns. If the trend continues, results could be severe and include melting of ice packs, flooding of low-lying areas, interruption of food production, and increased incidents of severe weather.

Electric power production is responsible for about one-third of the greenhouse gases emitted due to human activity in the United States, which is in turn responsible for roughly 14% of the world's greenhouse gas emissions. Greenhouse gas emissions are measured in units of tonnes of CO_2 equivalent. Coal generation is responsible for more CO_2 than any other generation source. (Coal generation emits about twice as much CO_2 per unit of output than natural gas generation.) Control technologies for CO_2 emissions from traditional power plants are being researched but are not currently commercially available.

GENERATION CHARACTERISTICS COMPARISON							
	Coal	**Nuclear**	**Natural Gas**	**Hydro**	**Petroleum**	**Wind**	**Solar PV**
Capital Cost	Medium - High	High	Low	Medium - High	Low	Medium	Medium
Variable Cost	Medium	Low	Medium	Low	High	Low	Low
Operational Flexibility	Medium	Low	High	High	High	Low	Low
Time to Permit and Construct	Long	Long	Short	Long	Medium	Short	Short
Environmental Impact	High	Low	Low	Low - High	High	Low	Low
Fuel Availability	Plentiful	Plentiful	Plentiful	Limited	Plentiful	Depends on Location	Depends on Location
Location	Remote	Remote	Near Loads	Remote	Near Loads	Remote	Remote if Utility Scale
Controllability	High	High	High	High	High	Low	Low

In late 2016 an international accord called the Paris Agreement went into effect. The accord was signed by 194 countries, and its goals included holding down the increase in global average temperature due to greenhouse gases, increasing the world's ability to adapt to climate change, making financing available for pathways to reducing greenhouse gas emissions, and achieving global peaking of greenhouse gas emissions as soon as possible. A number of countries including China, the U.S., and the member states of the European Union made non-binding commitments to achieve specific targets associated with limiting greenhouse gas emissions. In 2017, the U.S. administration announced that it would cease all participation in the agreement and planned to withdraw from the agreement completely by 2020. Meanwhile other countries continued their support although as of 2019 many have yet to meet their initial targets. In the U.S. numerous states, cities, and corporations stated their support for the agreement, and many took positive actions to reduce their greenhouse gas emissions. Thus as of 2019, the power generation industry's movement toward meaningful reductions of greenhouse gas emissions remains uncertain.

Demand Response and Energy Efficiency as Alternatives to Generation

An alternative to some generation is to develop mechanisms that reduce or shift timing of end-use demand. Such programs are called demand side management, or DSM. DSM includes energy efficiency, which reduces overall energy intensity for a specific use, and demand response, which reduces demand during peak times. Demand response (DR) can be emergency demand response (where customers are required to reduce demand only during times when their failure to do so will create reliability issues) or economic demand response (where customers are given economic incentives to reduce demand during times when it is cheaper to reduce demand than to purchase or generate additional units of electric supply and/or shift usage to times when plentiful renewable supply is available).

In the 1980s utilities implemented DSM programs in an effort to reduce the need for costly new generation construction. These programs encourage customers to implement energy efficiency measures through rebates for more efficient appliances and offer incentives such as discounted curtailable rate schedules that allow the utility to curtail service during times when high demand threatens system reliability. There has been a trend lately toward DR programs. These programs can have a significant impact on reducing peak loads, shifting loads to times with plentiful supply, and/or muting price spikes in competitive markets. Thus, utilities and retail marketers have an interest in creating means by which customers can be compensated for reducing demand upon request. Traditional rates that do not pass real-time price signals to customers fail to incent this behavior. DR programs include:

- Real-time pricing — Customers pay hourly prices that reflect same-day or day-ahead market conditions.

- Voluntary load response — Customers are offered a payment for curtailing blocks of load, usually in the day ahead.

- Curtailable capacity call — Customers are paid a capacity payment to give the utility or marketer the right to curtail blocks of load under certain conditions; failure to curtail results in payment of market rates for that block of load.

- Automatic load response — Customers are paid a capacity payment to give the utility or marketer the right to remotely and automatically curtail blocks of load.

With the growth in renewables, system operators now require increasing amounts of flexible resources and often experience significant shifts in costs of generation across the day. DR is becoming an increasingly common option for meeting system need for flexibility. As of 2017, the EIA estimated that over 9 million customers in the U.S. participated in demand response programs that saved over 1,300,000 MWh and reduced actual peak demand by over 12,000 MW.

Electric Storage

System operators must match supply to demand instantaneously across the hour. With fluctuating customer loads and increasingly variable supply from renewables, the ability to store and then withdraw energy from storage is a valuable tool in managing a grid. Historically, pumped hydro storage has provided the only economic means of storing electric supply. Pumped storage provides the capability of time-shifting energy between off-peak and peak hours and also can be used for short-term supply adjustments used for frequency regulation and spinning reserves. As of 2017, the U.S. had over 22,600 MW of pumped storage. But expansion of pumped storage is difficult given the need for specific resource capabilities, and it is not expected that pumped storage capacity will expand much in the near future.

Other methods of storing electric energy include batteries, thermal storage, flywheels, and compressed air energy storage (CAES). In the 2010s, battery costs declined rapidly making it feasible for batteries to be used as a grid storage resource. As of 2019, there is about 1,000 MW of utility-scale batteries installed in the U.S. The EIA forecasts that this will expand to over 2,500 MW by 2023. Batteries offer many grid benefits including frequency regulation, five-minute load following, spinning reserves, and local voltage support as well as time-shifting of energy over a few-hour time-frame. They can also be designed as part of a wind or solar project to provide more steady output. Many industry analysts expect that batteries will soon become an integral part of grid design and operations.

Use of Generation to Satisfy the Load Curve

The key to understanding electric supply markets is to understand which generating units are dispatched at what times to meet the load curve (the aggregate demand of all customers in a specific region). This has a major impact on wholesale electric markets since the cost of the last resource required in any given hour (the marginal cost) often determines the market price of electricity in competitive markets.

Generating units are typically scheduled hourly (one day in advance) based on least-cost supply subject to reliability, operating, locational, and regulatory constraints. Use

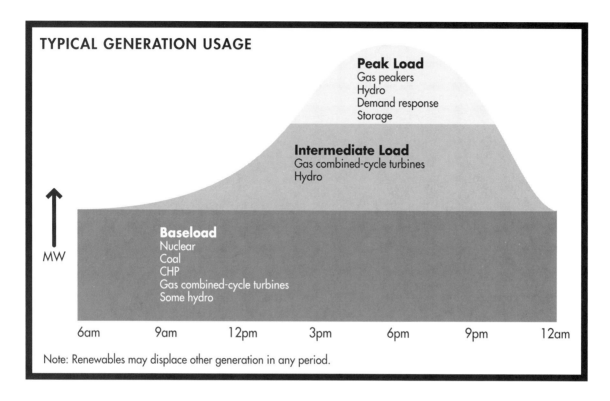

TYPICAL GENERATION USAGE

Peak Load
Gas peakers
Hydro
Demand response
Storage

Intermediate Load
Gas combined-cycle turbines
Hydro

Baseload
Nuclear
Coal
CHP
Gas combined-cycle turbines
Some hydro

MW

6am   9am   12pm   3pm   6pm   9pm   12am

Note: Renewables may displace other generation in any period.

4

of generation is often divided into three categories — baseload, which is generation run all 24 hours of the day; intermediate, which is run from mid-morning until the evening; and peaking, which is run during the peak hours (often from early afternoon until early evening). Units typically scheduled include:

Baseload

Baseload is typically satisfied by nuclear units, high-efficiency coal and natural gas units, wind, and hydro generation (all due to low variable costs), and Qualifying Facilities (due to regulatory requirements). In addition, system operators may schedule as baseload less efficient coal, gas, or petroleum generators that need to run to provide locational support to the grid (known as must-run generation). It is also sometimes necessary to run less efficient coal, gas, or petroleum steam turbine generators at minimum loads because their full capacity will be needed later in the day and their boilers must be kept warm so that the units can be ramped up for availability during the intermediate period.

Intermediate

Intermediate loads are often satisfied by coal units ramped up from minimum loads, combined-cycle gas turbines, and hydro power. These are used because their operational flexibility allows them to be ramped up and down as loads rise and fall during the day, and also because their variable costs are lower than other options. In some regions, wind or solar power also provides intermediate supply.

Peaking

Peaking loads are usually satisfied by single-cycle gas turbines (also known as peaking turbines), gas reciprocating engines, hydro power, pumped hydro where available, other forms of storage, economic demand response, and in some regions solar power.

Reserves

As we will learn in a later

WHAT IS A QUALIFYING FACILITY (QF)?

In 1978, the U.S. Congress passed the Public Utilities Regulatory Policy Act (PURPA), which contained measures to encourage more efficient use of energy resources. Among these provisions was a requirement that utilities buy the output of qualified cogeneration resources at the host utility's avoided cost rate, which is the cost the utility would pay to generate replacement power if the QF did not exist.

Pursuant to PURPA, the Federal Energy Regulatory Commission (FERC) set forth criteria for determining which facilities could receive Qualifying Facility (QF) status. To be a QF, a generating facility must produce electricity and another form of useful thermal energy (such as heat or steam) used for industrial, commercial, heating, or cooling purposes and must be less than 50 MW in size and meet certain ownership, operating, and efficiency criteria. Since investor-owned utilities are regulated by the states, FERC left it to them to define the avoided cost rate. Some states such as California initially set attractive QF rates resulting in significant development of cogeneration facilities (as much as 16% of the California ISO's supply comes from cogenerators), while other states set much lower rates and did not see much in the way of cogeneration development. QFs are typically located at large industrial facilities in industries such as food processing, refineries, and wood processing.

The Energy Policy Act of 2005 resulted in changes in rules for new QFs so that in competitive markets they will no longer receive regulatory-set pricing.

---

section, system operators must also schedule generation reserves to ensure system reliability. Good sources for reserves include hydro power, gas combined-cycle, combustion turbines, reciprocating engines, and coal steam turbine units that are running at partial capacity.

Flexible Generation

As penetrations of renewable energy grow, electric grids require increasing amounts of flexible resources that can compensate for the variability associated with wind and solar generation. Key sources of flexibility include gas combined-cycle, combustion turbines, reciprocating engines, hydro and pumped hydro units, batteries, and demand response.

Ownership of Generation

Prior to electric restructuring, virtually all the generation in the United States was owned by either investor-owned utilities, public utilities and rural co-ops, related generation and transmission agencies, or federal agencies. Since the advent of electric deregulation, a new category of generation owner has entered the market. These are non-utility generators, often called independent power producers (IPPs) or merchant generators. Non-utility generators are companies that own generation as a stand-alone business and not as part of a vertically integrated utility. These generators aim to own and operate their units for a profit by selling

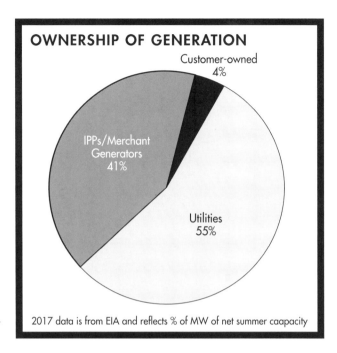

OWNERSHIP OF GENERATION

Customer-owned
4%

IPPs/Merchant Generators
41%

Utilities
55%

2017 data is from EIA and reflects % of MW of net summer caapacity

energy or capacity to utilities, marketing companies, and/or directly to end-use customers. In some states, utilities have divested of their generation assets by either selling them to non-utility generators or splitting the assets off from their utility function and creating their own non-utility generator subsidiary. In other states, non-utility generator ownership is limited to new units that have been built in recent years. Customer-owned generation is a final category and has been increasing in recent years.

Developing a Generation Portfolio

Companies that own generation must determine the best portfolio of generation units to satisfy the energy and capacity needs of their customers. In the past, this was a relatively simple task. Utilities responsible for providing supply start with their existing generation base, compare this against load forecasts, and then evaluate options to fulfill any additional supply requirements. Options might include modifications to existing utility generation, new utility generation, demand side management programs, purchased power (from neighboring utilities or non-utility generators), and new transmission lines to areas with excess generation. These options are then evaluated from the standpoint of cost and risk resulting in an integrated resource plan (see illustration on page 55). Integrated resource plans are typically filed with the state utility commission for approval before being implemented.

Non-utility generators must also evaluate generation portfolios, but their evaluation focuses on how to best create a return on shareholder investment. Thus a non-utility generator would carefully evaluate the market value of specific generating units as well as the strategic value of units relative to the company's other assets and business strategy (see box on page 56). Rather than an integrated resource planning process, non-utility generators use portfolio theory to attempt to maximize returns relative to perceived market risks.

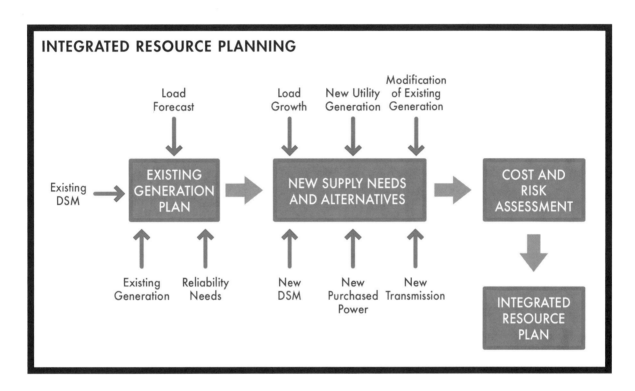

INTEGRATED RESOURCE PLANNING

In either case, generation planners must evaluate future load growth and the capability of existing generation to satisfy that growth, and then look for points in the load curve where new generation is needed.

The Future of Generation

Given the lead times necessary to construct new generation, owners are continually planning for the future. In some cases this involves retiring older units and replacing them with new and more efficient ones. In others, it involves building new generation to meet growing loads or needs such as renewable portfolio standards. Considerations in deciding what types of resources to build include capital costs, ongoing O&M, expected fuel costs, risks associated with fuel cost volatility, costs for future environmental mitigation, and market needs for specific characteristics such as flexible generation or renewable output.

As of 2019, the majority of new units planned for the U.S. are natural gas, wind, and solar generation. A large amount of coal generation is expected to be retired with almost no new units coming online. Although two new nuclear units are expected to come online in 2022, their output will be off-set by retiring older nuclear units. It should also be noted that the outlook for generation in the U.S. does not nec-essarily reflect the situation in other countries. Some regions of the world have plans to build significant amounts of nuclear and/or coal generation.

Technological innovation continues to drive changes in the generation mix. Development of the combined-cycle technology has made gas a favored fuel source in recent years. Substantial cost decreases in wind and solar driven by innovation in materials, design, and manufacturing have made these technologies a cost-effective alternative to fossil fuel generation. Construction of off-shore wind pro-jects may provide more steady wind resources. New technologies that may impact the future include integrated gasification combined-cycle units (IGCC), small modular nuclear reactors (SMR), and fuel cells.

IGCC units use coal as a fuel but eliminate many of the environmental concerns by gasifying the coal prior to combustion. This improves the efficiency of the combustion process and results in emissions that are similar to natural gas units. It is also possible through additional processes to remove most of the carbon prior to combustion, mak-ing IGCC even more environmentally attractive (see box on page 58). The carbon can then be sequestered by storing it underground to prevent its release into the atmosphere. Some in the utility industry are optimistic about IGCC (a few test units

---

FACTORS AFFECTING THE VALUE OF GENERATION

- Physical flexibility of unit

- Expected O&M costs

- Fuel efficiency

- Future price expectations for fuel

- Future price expectations for energy

- Future price expectations for ancillary services

- Expected price volatility and price spikes in each market

- Environmental and operating permit risk/benefit

- Location relative to transmission capacity

- Opportunity for reliability must-run contracts

- Opportunity to expand at site

- Impact on a company's sales strategies

- Impact on a company's risk portfolio

- The applicable discount rate of capital

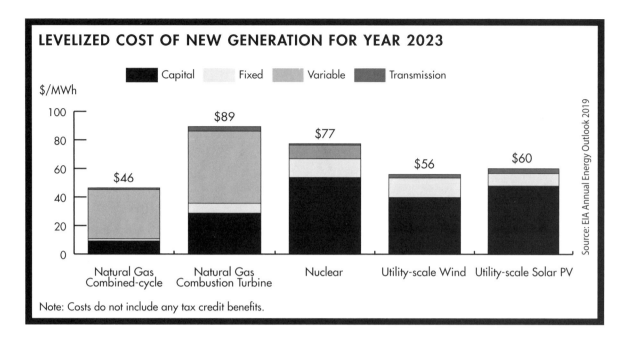

LEVELIZED COST OF NEW GENERATION FOR YEAR 2023

Legend: Capital | Fixed | Variable | Transmission

$/MWh

Natural Gas Combined-cycle: $46
Natural Gas Combustion Turbine: $89
Nuclear: $77
Utility-scale Wind: $56
Utility-scale Solar PV: $60

Note: Costs do not include any tax credit benefits.

Source: EIA Annual Energy Outlook 2019

are currently running) and believe this will become an important technology once cost barriers are overcome. Others believe the complexity of the technology will preclude its widespread use.

A significant barrier for future growth of nuclear generation is that current designs are for large units that usually exceed 1,000 MW. This typically requires investment of over $6 billion. Such an investment is difficult for companies unless they are a very large utility with regulatory guarantees of cost recovery or the investment is backed by government guarantees. And since the capacity of the unit is so large, it raises the significant possibility that the full amount of its output will not be needed until loads grow years into the future. In many parts of the world

U.S. SUMMER GENERATION CAPACITY CHANGES (PLANNED FOR 2018-2022)

Type	Additions (MW)	Retirements (MW)
Coal	1,142	22,817
Hydro	414	176
Natural Gas	60,738	11,007
Nuclear	2,200	9,475
Petroleum	40	586
Solar	14,204	2
Wind	25,981	20

Source: EIA Website 2019

CARBON CAPTURE AND SEQUESTRATION

Carbon sequestration refers to the capture and storage of carbon as an approach to reducing greenhouse gas emissions during the gas or coal generation process. In this process, carbon is removed, usually as carbon dioxide (CO_2), either prior to the combustion of the fossil fuel or after combustion in the exhaust stack. The CO_2 is then transported via pipeline or other means to a location where it can be stored. CO_2 might be stored in deep underground geological formations or in the ocean, or by transforming it into mineral carbonates. Most current research is focusing on geological formations. While carbon sequestration has been proven in concept, it is not yet developed for commercial-scale use. And the effects of long-term storage are still unknown. Costs of adding and operating technology for carbon capture and sequestration will certainly increase the cost of power generation. However, this concept may provide a useful tool in the battle to reduce greenhouse emissions from fossil fuel generation.

---

where competitive wholesale markets have evolved, including the U.S., these factors have been a huge barrier for nuclear power growth. One possibility that would make new nuclear power easier to finance and integrate into power systems would be construction of smaller units. Various nuclear companies are in the R&D phase of attempting to develop a cost-effective small modular nuclear reactor, or SMR. These units, typically in the 250 MW range, are conceived as modular units that would not need to be customized to specific sites and would better fit into financing capabilities and market needs. If development of a cost-effective SMR proceeds, growth in nuclear power may exceed current expectations.

Fuel cells may eventually change the way that we think about electric generation. A fuel cell is an electrochemical device that converts a fuel's chemical energy directly to electric energy. Fuel cells have no moving parts and are like a battery except that while batteries only store energy, fuel cells can actually produce electricity continuously given an ongoing supply of fuel. Fuel cells can run on various fuels including natural gas, gasoline, biogas, methanol, ethanol, and hydrogen. The big advantage to fuel cells is that with certain fuels their emissions consist of water and oxygen and thus are environmentally friendly at the point of generation. They are also well-suited to CHP applications. Some analysts believe that with technological advances, stationary fuel cells could become a valid option for widespread use in distributed electric production, thereby fundamentally changing our electric systems over the next 50 years.

While much of the discussion around new technologies still centers on centralized generation, some in the industry believe this is the wrong focus. It is possible that the industry will become increasing decentralized, with significant amounts of new resources being built on the distribution system. Many envision that a large number of

COULD THE FUTURE BELONG TO ZERO-CARBON GENERATION?

Can you imagine a world where fossil fuel generation is completely replaced with sources that emit no greenhouse gases? Many U.S. states and European countries can. As of 2019 California, Hawaii, and New Mexico have passed legislation setting 100% zero-carbon electricity mandates as have the countries of Denmark, Finland, France, Norway, Sweden, and the United Kingdom. A number of additional states and countries are considering similar requirements.

Falling costs for renewable generation and evolution of the grid have made plans for zero carbon feasible. Between 2009 and 2018, levelized costs for utility-scale wind power dropped by 69% while costs for utility-scale solar power dropped by 88%. A clean energy future that once looked very expensive has now become cost-competitive. Some regions are planning for 100% renewable generation portfolios while others will continue to make use of nuclear power in conjunction with renewable sources.

Key factors to make 100% zero-carbon possible include technological improvements and cost declines for battery storage, energy efficiency growth that reduces the amount of load that needs to be served, and flexibility in loads to allow electricity to be used when it is available from renewable resources (for instance, electric cars that can charge when power is available and stop charging when it is not). Also helpful is a robust transmission system that can move power across large geographic areas so that resources can be shared and balanced based on varying clean generation and customer demand in different regions. Will this occur? No one can say, but in recent years the concept has gone from fantasy to real possibility.

distributed energy resources including flexible demand response, distributed generation, and distributed storage will be orchestrated by distribution system operators to replace much of the supply currently provided by centralized power plants. The amount of distributed resources and their speed of growth will likely vary regionally with some regions moving toward distributed models in the next few years while others evolve more slowly.

What you will learn:

- What transmission is

- Types of transmission

- The physical characteristics of the transmission system

- Operation and planning of the transmission system

- Transmission system costs

- Ownership of transmission systems

- Issues with transmission system construction

- The current status of the transmission grid in the U.S.

- New smart grid technologies

5

SECTION FIVE: TRANSMISSION

Electric transmission is the movement of large amounts of electricity over long distances. In this process electricity is moved from a central generating unit to an interconnection with an electrical distribution system, or, in some cases, directly to industrial customers. The transmission system is the electrical highway that connects supply to demand across a network called an electric grid. Different entities define the facilities that comprise the transmission system somewhat differently, but transmission generally refers to any electric line with voltage greater than 60 kV (some entities use 40 or 50 kV as the break, some 115 kV). Typical transmission voltages in the U.S. include 69, 115, 138, 230, 345, 500, and 765 kV. In some regions the term subtransmission is used to refer to the circuits that serve distribution substations. Typical voltages include 34.5, 69, or 115 kV. Transmission lines can be designed to transmit either AC (alternating current) power or DC (direct current) power, but not both. Most lines in the U.S. are AC.

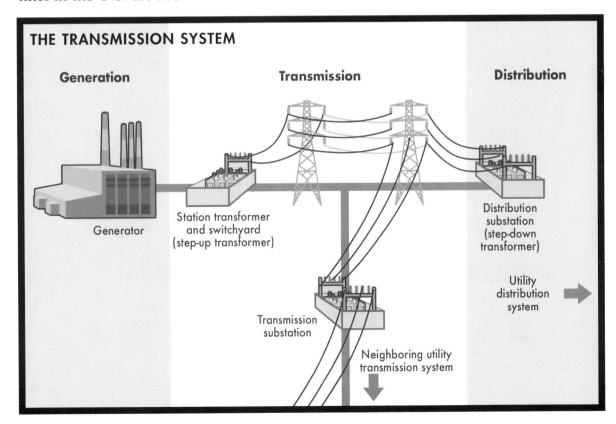

THE TRANSMISSION SYSTEM

Generation

Transmission

Distribution

Generator

Station transformer
and switchyard
(step-up transformer)

Transmission
substation

Neighboring utility
transmission system

Distribution
substation
(step-down
transformer)

Utility
distribution
system

Physical Characteristics of Transmission

In addition to transmission lines, the transmission system includes station transformers, switchyards, and transmission substations. Located outside of the generating unit is a switchyard where the station transformer increases the voltage of the unit output to the voltage of the transmission system. The switchyard also contains switches, breakers, busbars, and other protective equipment that configure the flow of power away from the generating unit and provide protection for both the unit and transmission grid. On the other end of the transmission system is the transmission substation, which is the interconnect to another entity's transmission lines. The substation contains switches, breakers and other protective equipment, monitoring and metering equipment, and, if necessary, transformers to adjust voltage between different incoming power lines. The transmission system connects to a distribution system at the distribution substation, which is generally considered part of the distribution system.

A key consideration in building transmission is to minimize capital and operating costs relative to the transmission capacity. Capacity is largely determined by wire size and voltage. High voltage transmission is the preferable way in which to move bulk amounts of power because higher voltages require lower currents. This reduces not only losses but also the size of the wire required to provide a specific transmission capacity — thereby reducing necessary capital investment. Transmission lines are generally situated overhead (above ground) except in dense urban areas where underground cables or busbar may be used.

The construction of much of the U.S. transmission network was completed during the 1960s and 1970s. Prior to 1950, maximum transmission voltages were typically 138 kV. From the mid-1950s through the 1960s, 345 and 500 kV systems were built. And by the early 1970s, lines with voltages as high as 745 kV were being added to the transmission system. Construction of

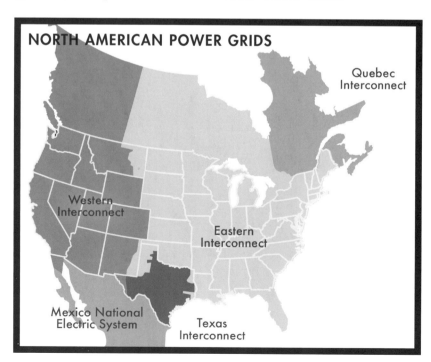

NORTH AMERICAN POWER GRIDS

Quebec Interconnect

Western Interconnect

Eastern Interconnect

Mexico National Electric System

Texas Interconnect

transmission lines usually occurs on a large scale since it is more economical to construct transmission lines with larger capacities.

By the late 1970s (after some 30 years of large-scale construction), we had reached a point where significant new construction was no longer required. In fact, there was even excess capacity in some areas. This, coupled with reduced growth in electricity demand and new technical innovations that increased the efficiency of existing lines, allowed the industry to minimize investments in transmission throughout the 1990s and to maximize the use of those investments already made. Developments in the 2000s including demand growth in certain regions, the growth of wholesale trading, construction of new generation, a major blackout in 2003, the need to integrate renewable energy in some regions, the use of locational pricing that makes transmission weakness transparent, and FERC incentives for new construction led to a resurgence in transmission construction later in the decade and on into the 2010s. As of 2018, the Edison Electric Institute projected that U.S. electric companies would spend over $20 billion per year on transmission projects over the next four years. This investment included new transmission expansion, replacement of existing transmission, system improvements, installation of new technologies, and security measures.

Over the years, utilities have interconnected their transmission grids for reliability and supply cost sharing purposes. In the U.S., the transmission system has evolved into three regional grids — the Eastern Interconnect, the Western Interconnect, and the Texas Interconnect. These regional interconnects, along with the Quebec Province grid in Canada, cover most of the U.S. and Canada as well as border areas of Mexico. The remainder of Mexico is covered by the National Electric System grid.

Operation and Planning of the Transmission System

Operation of the transmission system is integrally tied to both customer demand and to the operation of generation resources. Thus the generators and transmission systems must be operated in sync if they are to effectively respond to customer demand. This function is called system operations and is discussed in much greater detail in Section Seven.

An important function of system operations is to operate the transmission system at a capacity that will not harm the system. The optimal capacity of a transmission line is determined by three factors — thermal/current constraints, voltage constraints, and system operating constraints. Thermal constraints are limits set to avoid overheating a line. Due to resistance within the line, the flow of electrons causes heat to be produced. The temperature of a given line is determined by variable factors such as current flowing and ambient conditions such as temperature and wind speed (which affect dissipation of heat into the air). These factors can cause the line to overheat, which is dangerous because it can result in sagging (thereby putting the line in contact with trees or other conductors and potentially causing short circuits) and/or permanent damage to lines. To ensure the lines do not overheat, the system operator will set thermal limits on the system. Voltage constraints restrict the voltage that can be carried through a specific line. Excess voltages can result in short circuits, radio interference, and/or damage to transformers or customer equipment. And finally, system operating constraints are limitations associated with the need to maintain power flows throughout the transmission and distribution grids. Allowing too much power to flow on a specific line can result in redirection of flows that may interrupt proper operation of the grid.

The combination of transmission system capabilities and generation resources determines the reliability of supply available to a given region. Historically, transmission and generation resources were planned, built, and operated on an integrated basis by vertically integrated utilities. As certain areas of the country have moved into electric restructuring — resulting in the break-up of the vertical utility — operation and planning of the transmission system has fallen to Independent System Operators (ISOs) who operate separate and distinct from generation owners and distribution utilities. ISOs and regulators are working to develop new mechanisms to provide for sufficient transmission planning in a marketplace where generation is developed based on market conditions rather than on integrated plans associated with load growth.

Transmission System Costs

The bulk of costs associated with transmission service are the initial capital costs to build the lines. A lesser cost is the annual maintenance associated with keeping the lines operating reliably. Costs to build transmission lines vary from about $500,000 per mile for lower voltages (115 kV) to $1 million per mile for higher voltages (230 kV) to as much as $2-3 million or more per mile for ultra-high voltages (345 kV and above). The capacity of each line is also an important factor when considering cost. Underground transmission is significantly more expensive, often costing as much as 10 times more per mile than overhead.

Ownership of Transmission

Until the advent of electric restructuring in the U.S., transmission lines were owned by vertically integrated utilities, public power authorities, generation and transmission agencies, or federal generation agencies. As restructured electric markets have evolved, some utilities (at times at the request of regulators) have concluded that it no longer makes sense to own transmission lines and have sold theirs to transmission companies (also referred to as transcos). Some new transmission projects have also been built by transcos. A transco is a stand-alone owner of transmission facilities. Many industry observers believe that over time we will evolve to a market structure where transmission ownership and operation is dominated by transcos. This is similar in structure to the current U.S. interstate natural gas transmission system where investor-owned companies own and operate interstate pipelines as a stand-alone business.

Issues with Transmission Construction

Most experts agree that the U.S. electricity infrastructure needs considerable attention. Yet building new transmission lines is difficult. This is due to a number of factors that include public opposition, regulatory issues, and financial uncertainties. Public concerns about new transmission lines include land use issues, impacts on property values, environmental issues, and perceived electromagnetic field (EMF) threats. Local opposition is difficult to overcome when impacts may fall locally but benefits apply regionally.

Regulatory issues have also impeded new transmission construction. Key issues include mechanisms for recovery of costs and profits in rates, how costs are assigned to market participants, how projects that cross state lines can be effectively planned, and procedures for obtaining construction permits. Rates for transmission lines used for wholesale commerce are set by FERC. As deregulation of wholesale markets moved forward in much of the United States in the late 1990s and early 2000s, uncertainty over exactly how costs would be recovered slowed down investment in transmission. FERC responded by attempting to set specific principles for transmission rates and offering higher rates of return for new transmission construction. The issue of how transmission costs should be allocated persists, especially in ISO markets where they are potentially spread across a broad geographical area. It is not uncommon for participants in one region to oppose a project that they believe only benefits another region. Lastly, permits for construction are issued at the state level. This means that projects crossing multiple states must obtain permits from each state in a separate proceeding. Again, local interests may trump wider regional interests making it difficult to get all necessary permits.

To address some of these issues, FERC issued Order 1000 in July 2011 and Order 1000A in May 2012. These orders set guidelines for regional transmission planning including requirements that: each transmission provider participate in a regional transmission planning process that produces a regional transmission plan; these transmission plans provide an opportunity for new transmission projects to be built for public policy reasons beyond just reliability; and planning processes include coordination between neighboring regions for new interregional facilities. The orders also stipulated that existing transmission owners do not have the right of first refusal to build all new projects in their area and laid out principles for cost allocation for new projects including principles for regional and interregional cost sharing. FERC's goals in issuing the orders included fostering regional and interregional transmission construction in a cost-effective manner, fairly assigning costs of new transmission to parties that benefit from the new construction, and promoting competition in regional transmission planning.

Transmission Outages

As we will see in Section Seven, a key consideration in operating transmission is to avoid outages. Transmission outages can be caused by a variety of reasons including weather events, lightning, fires, malicious acts including vandalism and terrorism, failure of substation or circuit equipment, failure of protection systems, vegetation coming in contact with lines, unstable power system conditions, and human error. For 2017, NERC reported that the vast majority of transmission outage hours were due to equipment failure or weather. Of significant concern is the system's vulnerability to physical or cyber attacks. NERC Critical Infrastructure Protection (CIP) standards outline security protocols that must be followed by all transmission owners to mitigate those risks.

KEY CAUSES OF TRANSMISSION OUTAGES (2017)	
	% of hours
Failed Circuit Equipment	42.4
Failed Substation Equipment	21.6
Weather (excluding lightning)	12.5
Vegetation	4.3
Power System Conditions	3.4
Failed Protection Equipment	2.0
Fire	1.6
Human Error	1.5
Lightning	1.0
Other and Unknown	9.7
Source: NERC	

Transmission Smart Grid Technologies

In the 2010s, a number of updated transmission technologies became cost-effective, offering the opportunity for improved operation of the transmission grid. Technologies include:

- Phasor Measurement Units (PMUs) that allow monitoring of power characteristics.

- Power quality and flow control devices such as Flexible AC Transmission Systems (FACTS), Phase Angle Regulators (PAR), Static Var Compensators (SVC), Static Compensators (STATCOM), Thyristor-Controlled Series Capacitors (TCSC), and Thyristor Switched Series Capacitors (TSSC). These devices allow adjustments to maintain or control system parameters such as frequency, voltage, VARs, and/or line flows.

- Substation automation and substation monitoring devices such as Intelligent Electronic Devices (IED), Remote Terminal Units (RTU), Programmable Logic Controllers (PLC), and Programmable Automation Controllers (PAC). These devices provide local automatic condition response at the substation or provide for remote monitoring and control.

- Advanced IT systems that take advantage of the proliferation of smart devices including enhanced Energy Management Systems (EMS), real-time state estimators, system visualization tools, and Wide Area Management Systems (WAMS). These systems allow operators to make practical use of the information and control capabilities now available.

Here is an example of how new technologies can be used to increase the capacity of an existing transmission line. Traditionally, system schedulers used models to estimate the capacity available on transmission lines given expected weather, system flow, and other factors. Using estimated data and modeled conditions forced operators to be conservative since they had to be careful not to exceed physical line limits. This meant the true physical capability of lines often was underutilized. By installing and utilizing technologies that allow real-time monitoring and visualization of line conditions, operators can more fully use the capability of existing transmission lines.

The technologies that allow for real-time monitoring include devices capable of monitoring the condition of power flowing on transmission lines as well as devices that monitor physical factors such as line tension, line temperatures, and line sagging. This could be as simple as video cameras on top of towers that allow real-time visual monitoring for sag or may be as advanced as installation of PMUs at critical points in the grid.

PMUs allow visualization and monitoring of the magnitude and phase angle of system voltages and currents. Combined with analytical software, this data allows operators to analyze voltage, current, reactive power, and frequency at multiple locations throughout the grid. Given this knowledge, they can determine exactly what can and cannot be done on the transmission grid based on actual conditions.

What you will learn:

- What distribution is

- Types of distribution

- The physical characteristics of the distribution system

- Operation of the distribution system

- Distribution system costs

- Ownership of distribution systems

- The current status of distribution systems in the U.S.

- What a microgrid is

6

SECTION SIX: DISTRIBUTION

Electric distribution is the movement of electricity from the interconnection with the transmission system through the end-use consumer's meter. If transmission is considered the highway on which electricity travels long distances, the distribution system can be considered the streets and avenues that connect end-use customers to it. Generally, distribution refers to electric systems with voltages lower than 60 kV (although some utilities define distribution as lower than 40 kV). Distribution systems are often divided into primary systems (higher voltages) and secondary systems (lower voltages). Ultimately, the voltage at which electricity is delivered to an end-use consumer must be transformed to the voltage used by the consumer's electrical devices, which for smaller customers is the common 120 V we are used to seeing in our homes and offices. All distribution lines in the United States distribute AC power.

Physical Characteristics of Distribution

In addition to distribution lines, distribution systems consist of transformers, voltage regulators, switches, circuit breakers, automatic reclosers, power capacitors, monitoring systems, service drops, and customer meters. As mentioned above, the distribution system is generally divided into two categories — primary distribution (which is most commonly at voltages of 12.4 or 13.8 kV), and secondary distribution (which is most commonly at 120, 240, or 480V). Primary voltages are used to move electricity throughout the utility distribution area since distributing power at higher voltages results in less significant line losses. And secondary voltages are used as the lines approach a group of customers. Some industrial and large commercial customers take service at primary voltages (and in the case of very large industrial customers, even at transmission voltages). However, most customers — because they do not have the equipment necessary to transform it themselves — take voltage at the level

COMMON U.S. VOLTAGES
Primary Distribution
• 4,160
• 6,900
• 12,470
• 13,200
• 13,800
• 34,500
Secondary Distribution
• 120
• 240
• 480

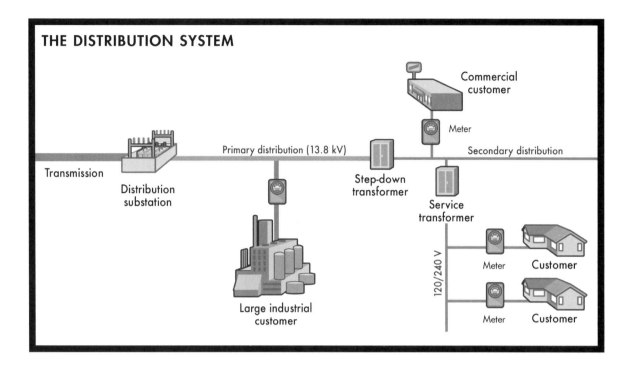

THE DISTRIBUTION SYSTEM

required by their appliances. In residential and rural areas, the most common supply voltages are 120/240, while in commercial or small industrial areas service voltages are 120/208 and 277/480 (dual voltages refer to the different voltages that are available at one service drop).

Power from the transmission grid enters the distribution system at the distribution substation. The distribution substation consists of transformers that step down voltages from transmission levels to primary distribution levels. After it is transformed, electricity leaves the distribution substation at the busbar, which is a large piece of metal conductor that allows multiple circuit connections. From the distribution substation, electricity is then distributed through the utility's service area in primary feeders. These carry the electricity to clusters of end-use customers and are also used to directly serve large customers who have their own transformers within their facilities. In areas with numerous smaller customers, step-down transformers reduce the voltage to secondary levels where it can be used by consumers. Depending on the voltage of the service line, a final transformer is often required outside the customer premises to provide the necessary service voltage. These are the transformers seen on poles in overhead areas, the pad-mount transformers seen as green cabinets (often outside commercial businesses), and the underground vault transformers located next to residential subdivision sidewalks. Distribution lines may be either overhead or underground. Overhead lines are cheaper to build and easier to fix, but are more exposed to potential hazards and in

VARs AND POWER FACTOR

A primary use of electricity is to drive electric motors. Electric motors create the mechanical energy of a spinning shaft by using electrons to create a magnetic field that causes the shaft to spin. The electricity that magnetizes the coils does no work. This is called reactive power, which is measured in units of volt-ampere reactive, or VAR. The portion of electric current that does work is called real power, which is measured in units of watts, kilowatts, etc. Historical electromechanical meters measure only real power although electronic meters can measure both.

The overall power that the system must be designed to deliver is called apparent power, which includes both reactive power and real power. Power factor measures the relationship of real power to apparent power:

$$\text{Power Factor} = \frac{\text{Real Power}}{\text{Apparent Power}}$$

VARs are produced by certain types of generators and can also be produced by other equipment such as capacitor banks placed on the distribution system. Since the utility needs to be paid for all the services it delivers, it prefers that customers have power factors as close to 1.0 as possible (since utilities bill customers for real power used in kWh, not for apparent power). For industrial customers, utilities will often measure the power factor at the meter and will bill industrial customers for power factor deviations outside of acceptable ranges. If these charges get too high, customers can install equipment on their side of the meter to better manage their power factor.

some areas are considered unsightly (i.e, unsightly enough to warrant the extra expense to bury them). Underground lines are more expensive to build and fix but require less maintenance and do not cause visual issues.

A key consideration for distribution lines is that they carry electricity safely and in a way that will not damage customer equipment. Thus the system is designed to quickly isolate short circuits and to maintain proper power quality (frequency and voltage). Voltage regulators ensure that system voltages remain within acceptable limits. Switches allow various circuits to be switched or connected to other circuits in different configurations. Circuit breakers are mechanical devices allowing circuits to be isolated (taken off the grid) so that maintenance can be performed and/or to protect the system in the event of power quality problems or circuit overloads. Automatic reclosers are circuit breakers that automatically interrupt circuits when a fault is sensed. Automatic reclosers give temporary faults repeated chances to clear themselves by closing a few times (often three times) before finally locking open and isolating the circuit if the fault fails to clear. These are commonly used throughout distribution lines as the first line of defense in minimizing power problems. Power capacitors are used in distribution systems to supply reactive volt-amperes (VARs) to support line voltage (see box above for explanation of VARs). At each customer location, a service run or drop consists of the cabling and protective equipment that connects the distribution system to the customer's internal wiring. And, of course, each utility must maintain a meter to measure the amount of energy used.

To ensure the system runs smoothly, the distribution facilities are monitored remotely using a SCADA (Supervisory Control and Data Acquisition) system. Typically SCADA systems are installed at concentrated points such as major substations so that the distribution operations center can monitor loads, status of circuit breakers, voltage, and VARs. Historically it has not been considered cost-effective to install SCADA systems throughout much of the distribution system, but as costs decline, more and more of the system is now remotely monitored and even controlled. And in some cases intelligent devices are economic to install on the system. These devices can make their own pre-programmed decisions on actions such as regulating voltage or even switching a line to self-correct an outage.

Distribution circuits are designed with specific customer loads in mind. Thus the size and type of circuit will be engineered based on the size and types of loads expected to be served. The addition of a major new customer or change in existing customer loads can often require reconfiguration or upgrading of a distribution circuit. Different types of distribution systems include radial feed, loop feed, and network system and are discussed in greater detail on the following page.

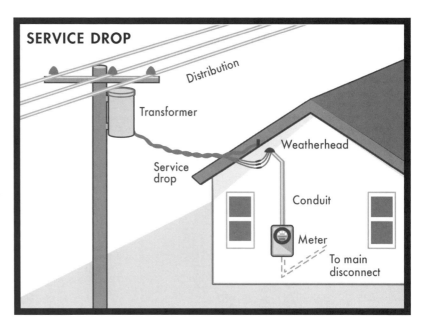

SERVICE DROP

Distribution

Transformer

Weatherhead

Service drop

Conduit

Meter

To main disconnect

SERVICE CONFIGURATIONS

Electrical services are provided in different configurations depending on the needs of the customers. Common variables for service are whether the service is single-phase or three-phase and whether the service is 2-wire, 3-wire, or 4-wire. Single-phase service is sufficient to operate typical lighting and small appliances and is generally what is provided to residential and many rural customers. Three-phase service is preferable where large motor loads exist and is commonly provided in commercial and industrial areas.

The number of wires refers to how many conductors are connected to the service. Electricians who wire buildings provide voltages to different types of electrical equipment by wiring the equipment to the conductors in different configurations. For instance, a 120/280 service would provide 120 V single-phase power for use by appliances and light bulbs while also providing for 208 V three-phase service for motors.

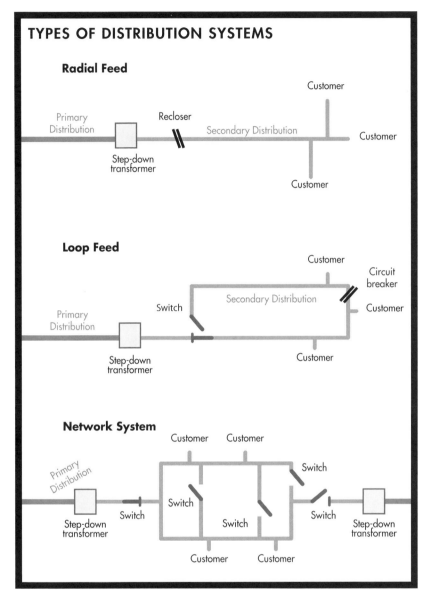

Radial Feed

A radial feed is simply a single line from a transformer out to a number of customers. While the lowest cost of the options, radial feeds do suffer from the fact that loss of cable, primary supply, or the transformer will result in loss of service to all customers on that feed. Also, radial circuits must be de-energized to perform routine maintenance and services.

Loop Feed

A loop feed serves customers off a loop that is connected to the primary feed at two ends. This costs more than a radial system since duplicative equipment is required, but it does provide the capability of isolating faults within the loop and continuing to feed all customers except those on the section with the fault. The reliability of both radial feeds and loop feeds can be enhanced by adding additional primary distribution feeds to the circuit.

Network System

A network system connects multiple primary feeds and interconnects multiple distribution circuits in the form of a grid. While network systems provide the highest form of reliability since customers can be served in multiple ways, they are also expensive because of the costs of duplicative equipment, transformers, and specialized network protective equipment. Networks are generally used in downtown urban areas with highly dense critical loads.

Operating and Planning of the Distribution System

Day-to-day operation of distribution systems is the responsibility of the distribution dispatch or distribution operations center. The dispatch center monitors flows and other system status values at points where SCADA systems have been installed. The dispatch center also directs system maintenance activities and oversees responses to any system outages or disturbances. During outages or disturbances, the dispatch center will direct crews on switching of circuits to restore power where possible and to ensure that lines are de-energized where crews are working. The dispatch center then restores the system to its normal operating configuration once appropriate repairs have been performed.

Maintenance management is a longer-term but similarly important function of operating a distribution system. Periodic routine maintenance as well as unplanned maintenance in response to system conditions must be performed to keep systems operating properly. A specific planned maintenance program is critical to prevent both deterioration of equipment as well as vegetation from growing into power lines. Identifying the equipment that is critical to safe operation of the system and developing contingency plans for its potential failure is also important.

Lastly, system planning studies are conducted periodically to determine the need for enhanced maintenance or system expansion. System models can be used to determine optimized operations and configurations, and overall system reliability and efficiency can be enhanced by frequently re-evaluating circuit design. And, of course, customer loads continually come and go, so system planners are always engaged in evaluating the need for system modifications to meet changing customer needs. As penetrations of distributed energy resources increase, planning studies must also evaluate the system's ability to integrate power put onto the system by customer-owned resources.

THE METER

The last key component of the distribution system is the meter located at each customer location. Without the meter, customers cannot be billed and energy companies cannot be paid. Metering is currently undergoing significant transition. Until recently, most meters were read once a month by a meter reader who recorded usage at each customer location. Meter data was generally limited to usage (kWh) and for larger customers maximum demand (kW). Since then we have become accustomed to increasingly sophisticated smart meters at reduced costs. Now many utilities depend on meters that can be read remotely and make meter data available on a real-time basis. Smart meters can be used to record large amounts of useful data including energy usage by time period, demand by time period, and various measures of power quality. In the next few years, the electric meter may evolve into a services gateway that will allow two-way communication between energy providers and consumers, opening up new ways for energy companies to maximize the efficiency of supply and customers to participate in energy markets.

Distribution System Costs

Because distribution systems are designed specifically to meet customer needs and no two distribution systems are the same, there is no rule of thumb concerning their cost. However, we can say that the portion of a customer's rate that reflects distribution costs is higher than the transmission component. It is also more costly to serve smaller customers than to serve larger customers since smaller customers are served at lower voltages and thus require more equipment. And it is significantly more costly on a per-customer basis to serve customers in either dense urban areas (need for underground service) or remote rural areas (need for a long distribution line to serve a small number of customers).

Ownership and the Current Status of Distribution Systems

Most distribution systems are owned and operated by a distribution utility. In some limited cases distribution systems are owned and operated by private entities such as military bases, large industrial complexes, or private developments. Distribution utilities can be divided into three categories — investor-owned utilities, municipal utilities (and their close cousins public utility districts), and rural electric co-ops. Investor-owned utilities, or IOUs, are for-profit companies owned by shareholders whose distribution functions are highly regulated by the state utilities commission. Municipal utilities and public utility districts are owned by local government entities, most commonly a city, and are usually not regulated by the state. Rural electric co-ops, also known as rural electric agencies (or REAs), are common in rural areas and are owned by their ratepayers and run by an elected board.

Distribution systems have been less affected by electric restructuring in the United States than have the generation and transmission sectors. An exception, however, is that many IOUs have been affected in regions where the vertical integration of generation, transmission, and distribution functions has been broken apart. This has forced the IOUs to restructure their business operations to create stand-alone distribution organizations. And in areas where customer access to alternative power suppliers has been allowed, the distribution function has been further restructured by eliminating the distribution utility responsibility for at least a portion of the supply function, although the utilities continue to distribute the power and ensure reliability regardless of who owns the power. Restructuring has generally not been applied to either municipal utilities or REAs, and most still operate as vertical utilities.

The Smart Grid

In the early 2010s, electric utilities began a transformation to what is known as the smart grid. While this transformation affects both transmission and distribution sectors, the effect will likely be greater on distribution since some of the components of the smart grid have been in use in the transmission sector for many years. In fact, since many of the smart grid technologies have already been in use in portions of the electric system, the transformation might be better described as moving from a somewhat smart grid to a smarter grid.

The term smart grid (also sometimes called the advanced grid) applies to deployment of various digital technologies at points throughout the transmission and distribution grid, and then implementation of internal procedures and external services that make use of the capabilities of the new technologies. These include integrated two-way communication technologies, advanced control methods, interconnected monitoring and metering equipment, advanced electronic grid components, decision support systems, and human interfaces. Key activities the technologies may enable include two-way communication with system components and with customers, real-time collection and presentation of system and customer data, improved grid modeling and real-time diagnostics, remote control of system and customer devices, automatic response to abnormal system conditions, information-based scheduling of maintenance, automatic outage detection and response, remote turn-on/turn-off of customers, remote meter reading, enhanced energy theft detection, integration of distributed storage and possibly electric vehicles, and implementation of advanced demand response and distributed generation services.

Distributed Energy Resources

By the mid-2010s, distribution utilities in many regions began the process of changing planning and design processes to account for increasing amounts of distributed energy resources (DERs) including rooftop solar and other distributed generation, advanced demand side management capabilities, and distributed storage. Integration of significant amounts of DERs may require circuit redesign to account for injections of supply on distribution circuits and, in some cases, even reverse flow of power from the distribution circuit back into the distribution substation. Areas requiring redesign include equipment for voltage and VAR management as well as protection schemes. Significant amounts of DERs also affect the distribution planning process. In some cases DERs can be managed so that line upgrades can be deferred or provide other

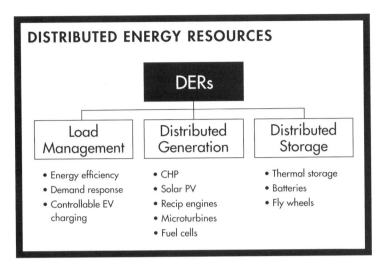

DISTRIBUTED ENERGY RESOURCES

DERs

Load Management	Distributed Generation	Distributed Storage
• Energy efficiency • Demand response • Controllable EV charging	• CHP • Solar PV • Recip engines • Microturbines • Fuel cells	• Thermal storage • Batteries • Fly wheels

benefits such as VAR management. In other cases, growth of DERs requires line upgrades. Some distribution utilities are moving toward a planning process that replicates the integrated resource planning used for central generation and transmission.

Microgrids

Also in the mid-2010s, utilities began to explore the benefits of including microgrids as part of the distribution system. Microgrids are small localized grids that can run in isolation but can also be interconnected into the wider grid. They may be owned by a customer behind a master meter, or they may be a portion of the distribution grid that can be isolated from the rest of the grid and still operated using local DERs. Why would anyone want to build a microgrid when they can simply be part of the traditional utility distribution system? One reason is the potential for higher reliability — microgrids can be built to deliver the level of reliability required by customers on the microgrid rather than the level of reliability applicable to generic utility customers. A second reason is that microgrids may provide economic benefits by allowing multiple facilities to interact with utilities and wholesale markets as an aggregated entity and to self-provide energy when economical. In this case, opportunities unavailable or uneconomical for smaller customers may become available when loads and distributed generation are aggregated.

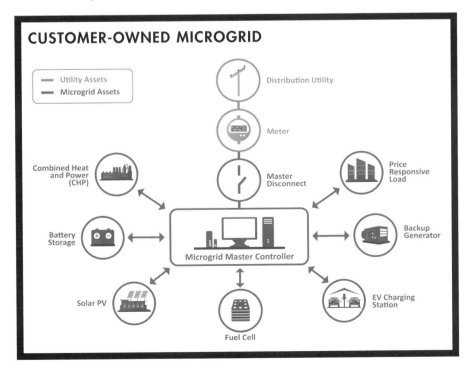

CUSTOMER-OWNED MICROGRID

Utility Assets
Microgrid Assets

Distribution Utility
Meter
Master Disconnect
Combined Heat and Power (CHP)
Price Responsive Load
Battery Storage
Backup Generator
Microgrid Master Controller
Solar PV
Fuel Cell
EV Charging Station

What you will learn:

- Operational characteristics of power systems

- The role of system operations

- Who is responsible for systems operations

- How system operations schedules supply, reserves, and transmission

- How supply and demand are matched in real time

- How the role of system operations is changing

- A typical day at an ISO

7

SECTION SEVEN: ELECTRIC SYSTEM OPERATIONS

The physical electric system comprises a highly complex and interdependent network of generators, transmission-level storage, transmission and distribution systems, distributed energy resources, and customer loads spanning thousands of miles. Despite the diversity of the system, it must always be controlled. Supply and demand must be kept in balance continuously, and voltages and frequencies must be kept within tight bounds or serious consequences may ensue: the customers' equipment may fail to run properly, grid equipment may be damaged, and, in the worst of scenarios, the system could crash and customers would experience outages. Managing this complex system in the short term (next day and next hour) and real time (current hour) is the responsibility of the electric system operator. System operators must schedule resources to ensure supply is available to match demand and, in real time, must continuously adjust supply levels to match demand fluctuations.

Operational Characteristics of Power Systems

Operating power systems is a complex task largely due to a few key physical characteristics. First, electricity cannot effectively be stored in transmission and distribution wires. This means that the supply coming onto the grid must be continuously balanced with the customers' usage. The operation of the system is further complicated by the fact that the path of electric flow is very difficult to control. Electrons simply flow on the path of least resistance, whether or not that path matches contractual agreements or the desires of the system operator. Thus interconnected utilities are inextricably entwined with the actions of their neighbors. The only way to avoid this interdependence is for utilities to isolate their systems. But because utilities depend on connections with each other for both reliability and access to economic supply sources, this is not a viable solution.

Further complicating system operations is the speed at which system disturbances travel. Changes in voltage or frequency on electrical lines travel at the speed of light, and any major system disturbances can be propagated across an interconnected grid in a matter of seconds. Disturbances can be dangerous because uniform voltages and frequencies must be maintained within strict limits to avoid degrading service to customers (e.g., voltage spikes knock off computers, low voltages dim lights, high frequency speeds the operation of electrical machinery and can damage generating equipment, etc.). And in an information society dependent upon computers and microchips, even momentary outages of computer-controlled equipment can cost customers millions of dollars and are not considered acceptable.

KEY CHARACTERISTICS OF POWER SYSTEMS

- Electricity cannot be stored in wires.

- Supply and demand must always be in balance.

- The path of electric flow is difficult to control.

- Disturbances travel very quickly.

- Voltages or frequencies outside of limits damage equipment.

- Even momentary outages are not acceptable.

What System Operations Does

System operators, also known as control area operators or balancing authorities, manage the actions of generators, other sources of supply, and transmission owners within their designated control area. They also coordinate with neighboring control areas, regional system operators, distribution operators, and other Load Serving Entities to maintain acceptable levels of service. To do this, the system operator must:

- Forecast demand in the day ahead.

- Schedule supply to match forecasted demand.

- Schedule reserves and other ancillary services.

- Schedule use of the transmission system among various market participants.

- Communicate schedules to neighboring transmission system operators so flows across interconnections can be anticipated.

- Communicate schedules to distribution operators and Load Serving Entities.

- Manage the system in real time by correcting imbalances every few seconds.

- Correct any system disturbances that may occur.

- Restore power should an outage occur.

Who Handles System Operations

North America has five regional grids made up of numerous interconnected transmission systems. These are the Eastern, Western, Texas, Quebec, and Mexico Interconnects (see map on page 62), and they generally operate independently of each other. Within each interconnect, however, utilities, transmission owners, and generators are tied together in a linked network so that the actions of any one system operator can have strong impacts on the others within their grid. Each interconnect is divided into various control areas. And for each control area there is a system operator that is responsible for system operations. System operators may be vertically integrated utilities, municipal utilities, federal power agencies, groups of utilities called power pools, or Independent System Operators (ISOs). ISOs are also sometimes certified by FERC as Regional Transmission Organizations (RTOs). Smaller utilities without a big enough system to warrant the cost of their own system operations often contract for the service with a larger neighboring utility, so control areas are often made up of multiple utilities. Some utilities have also banded together in groups called power pools that allow a pool of generators to be shared among utilities in order to optimize economic dispatch. In areas where generation markets have been restructured, the system operations function is taken over by the ISO (this has occurred to date in Alberta, California, Mexico, New England, New York, Ontario, Texas, and portions of the Mid-Atlantic, Midwestern, and Southeastern states), and the control areas become regional. Today North America has about 70 control areas that vary significantly in

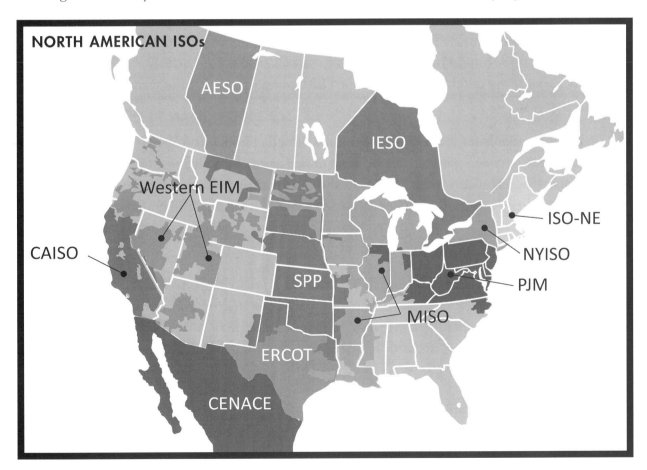

Demand Forecasting

Demand is forecast using models developed from historical demands given forecasted weather patterns and business activity. Using these models, system operators develop hour-by-hour day-ahead demand forecasts. Demand models are rerun during the day of delivery so that forecasts can be continually adjusted based on changes in weather or other factors.

Scheduling Supply, Transmission, and Reserves

Once the demand forecast is set, system operators then must schedule available supply to match demand. Supply alternatives may include non-variable generation, storage, demand response, forecasted variable generation output such as wind and solar, and imports from other areas. System operators then schedule supply on an hour-by-hour basis to match load and reserve requirements using an optimization principle called least-cost dispatch subject to constraints. Their goals are to optimize the schedule to ensure reliability standards are met and to minimize overall supply costs. Variables that must be considered in scheduling optimization include the ability of the transmission grid to move power to various parts of the system, generation that must be run to keep the system operating safely, and environmental and regulatory requirements. The physical ability of the system to serve all customers given a proposed schedule is determined by a power flow model. If the power flow model results in a non-feasible schedule, then schedules must be adjusted until feasible solutions are found. Generation that must be running to support the grid is called must-run generation, while generation that must be run for environmental and regulatory reasons (for instance, the requirement to take power from QFs) is called must-take generation.

Supply and transmission schedules are set forth on an hour-by-hour basis in the day ahead, and sources of supply are notified of their schedules. Units may be scheduled to provide energy (meaning they will be running) or to provide reserves (meaning they are ready to run as needed). In some cases, units may be scheduled so that a portion of the capacity is used for energy and the rest is used for reserves — for example a 400 MW unit might be scheduled to provide 300 MW of energy and 100 MW of reserves. On the day of delivery, unit schedules may be adjusted in the hour ahead based on changes in the forecast.

SIMPLE EXAMPLE OF SCHEDULING

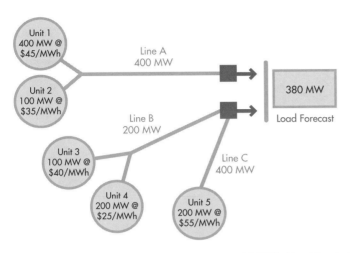

In this simple model, system operations has forecast 380 MW of load for the hour. In attempting to optimize scheduling (lowest to highest cost generation), the system operator would prefer to schedule:

Unit 4	$25	200 MW
Unit 2	$35	100 MW
Unit 3	$40	80 MW

Unfortunately, this is clearly not feasible given the limited capacity of transmission line B (only 200 MW). So the optimized dispatch, subject to constraints will be:

Generation Schedule

Unit 4	$25	200 MW
Unit 2	$35	100 MW
Unit 1	$45	80 MW

Transmission Schedule

Line A	180 MW
Line B	200 MW

In addition to the units scheduled for energy, the operator will also need reserves. Since the greatest single loss contingency is 200 MW on Line B, the operator will need to schedule 200 MW of reserves. The safest place to obtain the reserves is from Unit 5, since the loss of Line A would create a situation where reserves from Unit 1 would not be available to the system. If Unit 5 is scheduled for reserves, this would also necessitate scheduling Line C for 200 MW to ensure the transmission capacity is available if supply from Unit 5 is needed.

Ancillary Services

Ancillary services refer to the services (other than energy) required by system operators to ensure safe and secure operation of the electric grid. Ancillary services include:

Automatic Generation Control (AGC)

Also called regulation, AGC is used to manage the minute-by-minute fluctuations in system loads. AGC units can be ramped up and down remotely from the system operations software and are used throughout successive five-minute periods to keep supply and demand in balance. Typical sources of AGC include hydro power, gas combustion turbines, and gas or coal steam turbine units that are providing energy from a portion of their capacity but have additional unused capacity. In some control areas, batteries, fly wheels, and flexible loads also provide AGC.

Load-following Resources

Load-following resources are used to manage fluctuations in system loads over a longer time period than AGC, typically five minutes. Every five minutes, the system operator evaluates the load/generation balance and determines whether operating units need to be ramped up or down. Load-following resources are used in conjunction with AGC to keep the system balanced across each hour. Typical load-following resources include hydro power, gas combustion turbines, gas combined-cycle turbines, and gas or coal steam turbines.

Spinning Reserves

Spinning reserves refer to units or portions of units that are not putting energy onto the grid but are already synchronized to the frequency of the system and thus can begin providing energy upon receiving a dispatch call. Capacity included in spinning reserves must be fully available to the system operator within 10 minutes of notification. Typical sources of spinning reserves include hydro power, gas combustion turbines, and gas combined-cycle and gas or coal steam turbine units that are providing energy from a portion of their capacity but have additional unused capacity. In some cases demand response can also be a source for spinning reserves.

Non-spinning Reserves

Non-spinning reserves are units that are not synchronized to the frequency of the system but can be available within 10 minutes of notification. Non-spinning reserves can also include demand response that is available within the 10-minute window. While non-spinning reserves have the same 10-minute requirement as spinning reserves, these units take longer to begin contributing partial generating capacity since they must first be synchronized to the system. Typical sources of non-spinning reserves are similar to those used for spinning reserves.

Supplemental Reserves

Supplemental reserves are units that are available with a longer lead time, often 30 minutes from notification. Typical sources for supplemental reserves are coal and gas steam turbine units that already have warm boilers.

Flexible Ramp Capability

With the growth in renewable resources, short-term supply variability has increased. To address this issue some ISOs have introduced a new ancillary service that pays sup-

CASCADING OUTAGES

Blackouts generally begin when a large transmission line or generating unit suddenly drops off-line due to an unexpected event. Examples include power lines coming in contact with trees, lightning strikes, or equipment failures. Normally, power system operators are able to compensate for the loss of one source of supply by rapidly bringing on reserve sources so that supply and demand stay in balance. But if the system is already running tight due to a prior incident, or if system response is inadequate due to physical circumstances, equipment failure, and/or operator error, additional system disturbances may occur. As supply and demand get out of balance in a certain region, voltage and frequency spikes begin to propagate through transmission lines. Because these spikes can be damaging to equipment, transmission lines and generating units have automatic or manual relays that are designed to island troubled areas from the rest of the interconnected grid. If islanding is done quickly and surrounding areas have adequate generation to support their demand, blackouts can be limited to a small area. However, if efforts to island the disturbance fail, the problems will continue to cascade throughout the interconnected grid. Although rare, cascading blackouts do occur. The most recent large-scale event was the blackout on August 14, 2003, which affected over 50 million people in the Midwest, Northeast, and Ontario. Following are details of some of the major outages over the last 40 years:

Date	Locations Affected	Customers Affected	Duration
November 9, 1965	Virtually all of NY, Connecticut, Massachusetts, Rhode Island, and much of Ontario	30,000,000 customers, 20,000 MW of demand	Up to 13 hours
July 13, 1977	New York City	9,000,000 customers, 6,000 MW of demand	Up to 26 hours
July 2, 1996	Arizona, California, Colorado, Idaho, Montana, Nebraska, Nevada, New Mexico, Oregon, South Dakota, parts of Texas, Utah, Washington, Wyoming, Alberta, British Columbia, and Baja Norte	2,000,000 customers, 11,850 MW of demand	From a few minutes to several hours
August 10, 1996	Arizona, California, Colorado, Idaho, Montana, Nebraska, Nevada, New Mexico, Oregon, South Dakota, parts of Texas, Utah, Washington, Wyoming, Alberta, British Columbia, and Baja Norte	7,500,000 customers, 28,000 MW of demand	Up to 9 hours
June 25, 1998	Minnesota, Montana, North Dakota, Wisconsin, Ontario, Manitoba, and Saskatchewan	152,000 customers, 950 MW of demand	19 hours
August 14, 2003	Parts of Ohio, New York, New Jersey, Michigan, Pennsylvania, Connecticut, Massachusetts, Vermont, and Ontario	50,000,000 customers, 61,800 MW of demand	Up to 2 days, rolling blackouts in Ontario for up to one week
September 8, 2011	Parts of Arizona, California, and Baja Norte	2,700,000 customers, 7,835 MW of demand	Up to 12 hours

You may remember that California instituted rolling blackouts during the California energy crisis of 2000-2001. These blackouts were not the result of a cascading outage but were planned load reductions to keep demand in balance with limited electric supply.

ply sources for the capability to ramp up or down between load-following intervals without using up AGC resources. These products are sometimes designed to "look forward" across five-minute intervals to ensure sufficient ramp capability in future intervals within an operating hour (as opposed to AGC and reserves requirements that are set at the start of a given hour). Typical units providing flexible ramp capability are hydro units and natural gas combustion or combined-cycle turbines.

Voltage Support

Voltage support is provided by specially equipped units that have the capability to provide VARs to the system (for an explanation of VARs, see box on page 71).

Blackstart

Most units cannot start up without electricity from the grid. This causes a problem for restoring the grid if an outage has occurred. Blackstart units can start independently without electricity from the grid. System operators need to maintain a certain amount of blackstart to ensure their ability to restore the grid should there be an outage.

Once units have been scheduled to provide any of these ancillary services in the day ahead, the plant operators are told how they are expected to operate each hour of the day for the following day. However, these schedules may be adjusted in the hour ahead (actually two hours prior to operation) if forecasts or unit or transmission line availability change.

How Supply and Demand Are Kept in Balance in Real Time

After the system operator has forecast demand, scheduled the system in the day ahead to meet the forecasted demand, and then adjusted that schedule in the hour ahead, he must then monitor and manage the system in real time. During the hour, the system operator will normally keep the system in balance by ramping AGC and load-following units up and down in response to load fluctuations. If loads are higher than forecast, or sources of supply are lost unexpectedly and AGC and load following is not sufficient, then the operator will call on spinning reserves to keep the system in balance. This, however, leaves the operator short on spinning reserves should another unexpected event occur. It is likely that he will then move non-spinning reserves to spinning status, or move the non-spinning reserves directly online as energy, and then ramp the spinning units back down once the additional generation from non-spinning resources becomes available. In this way the operator can maintain the system within the NERC criteria even during contingency events.

Occasionally, despite the best efforts of system operators, the system will get out of balance. The result is voltages and/or frequencies outside the accepted limits. High voltages or frequencies are managed by reducing supply, while low voltages or frequencies require increasing supply. The last line of defense against low voltages or frequencies is to take loads off-line to get supply and demand back in balance. Many utilities have interruptible customers whose supply can be interrupted for reliability reasons. As a last resort, the system operator may need to involuntarily interrupt customers by isolating their circuit from the grid. This is called a rolling blackout.

The Value of Large Geographical Dispatch

As ISOs have expanded, the value of optimizing dispatch across large areas has become clear. For example, in 2013 six Entergy operating companies spread across the states of Arkansas, Louisiana, Mississippi, and Texas joined the Midcontinent ISO (MISO). Two years later, Entergy reported that joining MISO had resulted in annual savings of over $230 million. Benefits included reduced use of costly inefficient generation and lower requirements for reserves.

Across the Western United States, multiple utilities have combined with the California ISO (CAISO) to create the Energy Imbalance Market (EIM). This is an automated real-time energy wholesale market that matches the lowest-cost supply with demand every five minutes and dispatches units across parts of British Columbia, Arizona, California, Idaho, Nevada, Oregon, Washington, Wyoming, and Utah. What is unique about the EIM is that utilities from states without an ISO have voluntarily agreed to participate in the CAISO real-time market. Participation provides more opportunity to integrate variable resources such as wind and solar, as well as economic benefits by providing a mechanism for identifying and dispatching the lowest-cost resources across the market area. As of 2019, participating entities include nine utilities and/or control areas with eight more scheduled to join in the next three years. CAISO has estimated that the market created benefits of $650 million from its start in 2014 through the first quarter of 2019. Given the success of the EIM, SPP proposed in 2019 to create a similar Western Energy Imbalance Service that it intends to launch by 2020.

Scheduling in Regions with High Penetrations of Variable Supply and Distributed Energy Resources

Because renewable resources such as wind and solar have almost no variable costs, they are commonly the lowest-cost resource in a region. So the system operator will schedule as much renewable supply as the system can physically accept. A second resource that may not be controlled by the system operator is distributed energy resources (DERs). DERs are typically under the control of their owners who operate them for the purposes of bill management or revenue generation under local utility rules, rather than as active market participants in wholesale markets. When scheduling, system operators must take into account variable supply as well as other DERs or day-ahead forecasts will not be accurate. System operators utilize the concept of net load to determine how much non-variable centralized generation (such as gas, hydro, and coal units) to schedule for each hour. As variable and distributed resources grow, the shape of the net load curve begins to look very different from traditional curves.

In the example on page 92, the net load is about 1,000 MW below total load in the night hours due to wind output. As the system gets into the morning hour, total load grows as wind output drops. Then in mid-morning, solar output quickly increases, pushing the net load to its lowest level across the whole 24-hour period. As the sun sets, net load grows quickly due to the loss of solar power. But price-based demand response and battery discharge to capture high prices mutes the overall net load level in the early evening hours. So as you can see, system operators have a lot more to

7

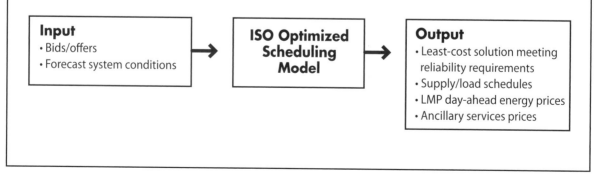

A TYPICAL DAY AT AN ISO

To prepare for the next day, the ISO must schedule supply across the coming 24 hours. This is handled by the day-ahead scheduling process. Supply is scheduled hourly, meaning that providers receive 24 schedules — one for each hour of the following day. The schedule tells each provider which services it is expected to provide and the amount of MWs associated with each scheduled service. For instance, for a given hour a power plant with a capacity of 200 MW might have 150 MW scheduled to provide energy and 50 MW scheduled for spinning reserves. So for the given hour, the power plant is expected to provide 150 MW of energy and must also be prepared to ramp up an additional 50 MW if called on by the ISO.

The day-ahead process works as follows:

- At a specified time in the morning each unit scheduling coordinator submits an offer to the ISO. This offer includes services the provider is willing to provide at a given price as well as various operational characteristics such as start time, ramp capability, willingness to be started and then stopped, and minimum and maximum run times.

- Simultaneously, Load Serving Entities (LSEs) submit hourly bids for buying energy to supply loads. Although LSEs sometimes state an unwillingness to buy energy above a certain price level, in most cases LSEs simply state a forecast load plus a willingness to pay whatever the price is to receive supply.

- The ISO inputs expected system conditions including transmission and variable resource availability and then runs optimization software to determine the least-cost dispatch available to serve the required loads given the various supply offers.

- By the early afternoon, the ISO sends out schedules to each provider that was selected in the optimization process and notifies others that they have not been scheduled. The ISO also notifies all LSEs of the amount of load that has been scheduled to be served. The optimization model also creates day-ahead energy prices for each location on the grid and zonal prices for ancillary services. The energy prices are called Locational Marginal Prices, or LMPs, and reflect the actual marginal cost of serving load at each location.

- Since day-ahead schedules are considered firm, supply providers are paid the LMP for their scheduled output and loads are charged the LMP for their scheduled deliveries regardless of what actually happens in real time.

A separate group at the ISO runs the system to ensure that supply and demand are kept in balance in real time. This process works as follows:

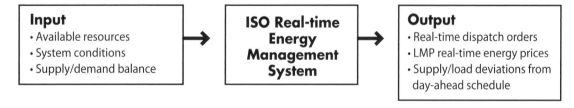

Input
- Available resources
- System conditions
- Supply/demand balance

ISO Real-time Energy Management System

Output
- Real-time dispatch orders
- LMP real-time energy prices
- Supply/load deviations from day-ahead schedule

- The real-time operators have various sources of supply available to ramp up or down given the resources selected in the day-ahead scheduling process.

- As the supply-demand balance fluctuates, the ISO ramps supply as needed based on the offers accepted in the day ahead. A real-time LMP is determined based on the price for marginal supply used in ramping.

- After the hour, the ISO calculates each unit's actual output compared to the output scheduled in the day ahead. The real-time LMP is applied to any deviation from what was scheduled, and each provider is paid or charged (depending on whether it supplied more than scheduled or less than scheduled) based on the LMP at its location.

- Similarly the ISO compares each LSE's schedule at specific grid locations to the LSE's actual usage. Again, any deviation from the day-ahead schedule is either charged or paid depending on whether the LSE used more or less than scheduled.

think about than they used to when they just had to schedule controllable power plants and predictable consumer usage.

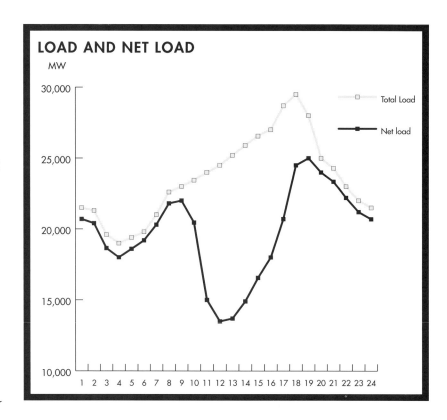

LOAD AND NET LOAD

The Changing Role of System Operations

In this section, we have described the physical actions that a system operator must take to ensure reliable operations of the grid. We have not discussed the market structures that are necessary to make resources available to the system operator nor the commercial mechanisms for determining how those resources should be scheduled and paid for providing services. Historically, system operations has been handled by a vertically integrated utility or a power pool that has direct control over all the units on its system. In this simple structure, units are scheduled based on marginal costs of operation and any system constraints. As parts of the U.S. have moved into competitive electric markets, the necessary commercial arrangements have become much more complex. Now system operators are asked to balance supply and demand when demand is served by numerous competing entities and generating units are owned by a multitude of profit-driven merchants. Keeping the system working requires a carefully crafted set of market arrangements. Different market structures have been tried — some have worked well and others have failed notably. In Section Nine we will address the various market structures and the related trading arrangements and rules for scheduling systems in competitive environments. But first we'll take a look in Section Eight at the various market participants in the vertically integrated and restructured models.

What you will learn:

- Who market participants in the traditional vertically integrated marketplace are

- Who market participants in the competitive market models are

- The roles of the various market participants

SECTION EIGHT: MARKET PARTICIPANTS IN THE DELIVERY CHAIN

Because the different market structures found in the U.S. alter both the makeup and roles of market participants, we need to discuss these entities twice. We'll first discuss participants in the traditional vertically integrated utility market model, then we'll look at the various market participants in the more complex competitive models. We will discuss the market models themselves in the following section.

Participants in the Vertically Integrated Market Model

The historic U.S. market model is simply a vertically integrated monopoly that handles all electric service functions as an integrated entity. This means the utility owns the generation and transmission necessary to serve its end-use customers, manages system operations to serve them, and is the only entity providing electric distribution and supply. Different types of integrated monopoly utilities include investor-owned utilities, munis, and co-ops.

Investor-owned Utilities

Investor-owned utilities, or IOUs, are for-profit corporations owned by either public or private shareholders. Most are publicly owned and their stocks trade on Wall Street. Others are owned by private equity. Because these entities are for-profit, they must be regulated to ensure that the interests of consumers are being preserved. Each IOU is assigned a specific franchise service territory and is responsible for serving all electric consumers within that area. No other entity is allowed to provide electric distribution services in the IOU's service territory. Traditionally, IOUs owned all their own generation, transmission, and distribution and managed their own system operations. Due to a federal regulation called PUHCA that was repealed in 2005, IOUs were mostly prohibited from crossing state lines, and thus a fragmented market of numerous IOUs evolved. IOUs typically interconnect, however, and trade with each other to take advantage of cost and reliability benefits. The U.S. has about 200 IOUs that serve about 68% of the customers in the U.S.[1] While in some cases multiple IOUs are

---

[1]Data from the American Public Power Association 2018 Stats and Facts.

owned by the same corporate holding company and some functions are centralized, each IOU is still run as a separate company for regulatory purposes. Examples of large utility holding companies include AEP, CenterPoint, Duke, Entergy, Exelon, First Energy, and Southern Company. Examples of large IOUs include Florida Power and Light, Pacific Gas and Electric, Southern California Edison, Consolidated Edison, and Xcel Energy.

Municipal Utilities and Public Utility Districts

In some areas, local governments are responsible for providing electric services rather than allowing for-profit IOUs to handle them. In many cases, these utilities are run by the city government and are called municipal utilities, or munis. In certain states, these utilities are run by a group of cities, a county, an irrigation district, or another public entity and are called public utility districts, or PUDs. Munis and PUDs are non-profit organizations that are run by a local government agency. Municipal utilities generally operate as a division of the local city government and provide electricity in the same way that many cities provide water, sewer, garbage, and other utility services. In most states, they are not regulated by the state. Larger municipal utilities may own their own generation, transmission, and distribution facilities and may also perform their own system operations. Smaller munis usually band together to create public power agencies that share ownership of generation and transmission. Virtually all munis own and operate their own distribution systems[2]. Many munis also buy power directly from federal power agencies and, in recent years, have commonly traded power with IOUs and other parties. The U.S. has over 2,000 munis and PUDs that serve about 15% of end-use customers. Examples of large munis and PUDs include the Salt River Project, the City of Los Angeles, CPS Energy, the City of Memphis, Jacksonville Electric Authority, and Sacramento Municipal Utility District.

Rural Electric Co-ops

As the electric grid evolved in the United States, neither municipal utilities nor IOUs had much interest in building costly distribution systems into rural areas. Given concerns about quality of life and the sustainability of agriculture, the federal government created in 1936 the Rural Electrification Administration, which provided for the creation of rural electric co-ops. Co-ops are utilities owned by their customers (called

---

[2]The exception is that in recent years some municipalities have created aggregation utilities. These do not own facilities but buy power on behalf of their citizens and use the IOU's distribution system to deliver that power to customers. In California, where this has become popular, these entities are called Community Choice Aggregators (CCAs). As of 2019, eight states had enacted CCA legislation including California, Illinois, Massachusetts, New Jersey, New York, Ohio, Rhode Island, and Virginia.

members) and run by an elected board. Co-ops own all the distribution lines within their area and provide all electrical service to their customers. Many co-ops are distribution-only utilities that purchase their power from federal generation agencies. In cases where there is not enough federal generation available, groups of co-ops have banded together regionally to create generation and transmission cooperatives that own facilities on behalf of the distribution co-ops. Co-ops are operated as not-for-profit organizations, and any excess funds collected are returned to the members at the end of the year. The U.S. has just under 900 co-ops that serve about 13% of U.S. customers. Examples of co-ops include Jackson EMC, Middle Tennessee EMC, Rappahannock Electric Cooperative, Volunteer Energy Cooperative, and Connexus Energy.

Federal Power Agencies

Federal power agencies are entities created by the U.S. government to market the power output of federal projects — primarily hydro power on federal dams. There are four federal power agencies: Bonneville Power Administration (BPA), Southwestern Power Administration (SWPA), Southeastern Power Administration (SEPA), and Western Area Power Administration (WAPA). The federal power agencies generally perform the role of generation provider to a vertically integrated public utility sector (i.e., to munis, PUDs, and co-ops). Due to federal law, preference in the sale of federal power must be given to public bodies and co-ops. IOUs can buy federal power only if it is surplus power that cannot be sold to the preference customers. In some limited cases, the agencies are also authorized to sell directly to large industrial customers. The agencies also own transmission lines that run from their projects to other utility-owned grids. In some cases, such as in the western U.S., these transmission lines can be quite extensive. In these areas it is common for the federal power agency to also assume the system operations function.

Similar in some ways to the federal power agencies is the Tennessee Valley Authority (TVA). TVA is a corporation owned by the United States government. TVA provides wholesale electricity in seven southern states as well as services such as flood control, navigation, economic development assistance, and land management for the Tennessee River system. TVA owns coal, natural gas, hydro, nuclear, and renewable power plants and also purchases renewable energy from project owners. It sells most of its power output to municipal utilities and co-ops, but it also serves large industrial customers and government facilities directly as a retail provider and sells excess wholesale power into regional power markets.

Public Power Agencies

As described above, smaller municipal utilities, PUDs, and co-ops often work together to own generation and transmission. They do so by creating entities called public power agencies or joint power authorities. These agencies are owned by the participating utilities and take on the responsibility of owning and operating generation and transmission facilities. By joining together, the smaller utilities are able to share the costs and risks of owning and maintaining the facilities necessary to serve their customers. In a few limited cases, power authorities are owned by a state government. These authorities typically own generation and transmission.

Power Pools

Power pools are created by groups of utilities that turn over to them the scheduling and dispatch function for their power plants. The concept behind the power pool is that multiple utilities within a region can gain higher reliability and lower costs by placing their generation assets into a regional pool. The units can then be operated on a regional basis. This results in cost savings to all participating utilities since higher-cost utilities have access to generation that may be lower-priced than their own, and lower-cost utilities receive additional power sales revenues. By using a pool, utilities do not need to continually rely on trying to trade power to obtain the savings but rather can obtain them through the routine scheduling and dispatch process. Power pools were used extensively in the northeastern U.S. prior to deregulation, but the largest of the pools — PJM, New England, and New York — have now been replaced by ISOs.

Energy Services Companies (ESCOs)

Energy services companies, or ESCOs, evolved in the regulated model to offer services beyond the regulated services offered by utility companies. Typical ESCO services include bill evaluation, demand side management, appliance maintenance, power reliability, and power quality. These services are provided by numerous for-profit organizations, both large and small, and are in addition to regulated services offered by utilities.

Independent Power Producers and Electric Marketers

As competition came into vertically integrated markets, limited roles for independent power producers (IPPs) and electric marketers evolved. Independent power producers are non-utility for-profit companies that own generation and sell the output to utilities under long-term contracts. Electric marketers are entities that buy excess supply from generators and/or utility companies and resell the power to other market participants.

These roles are generally very limited in the vertical utility model, and we will discuss them in more detail later in this section. In a vertically integrated market, the role of the IPP is to offer an alternative to utility-financed construction. For example, a utility that needs 200 MW of new supply might find it advantageous to contract with an IPP rather than building the capacity itself.

Participants in Restructured or Competitive Electric Markets

As electric markets are restructured to allow competition in the generation or retail sales sides of the business, roles are opened for a significant number of new market players. We will explore different competitive market structures in Section Nine, but for the purposes of this discussion it is important to understand that restructured markets typically move generation, system operations, and retail sales (meaning the sale of electric supply to end-use customers) outside the purview of the monopoly utility. The utility becomes a transmission and distribution (or sometimes just distribution) organization that delivers electricity to end-use consumers on behalf of other market participants.

Merchant Generators and IPPs

Merchant generators and IPPs are independent owners of generation that are not part of the regulated utility. They own and operate generation in the interests of making a profit for their shareholders. Some in the industry differentiate between IPPs, who tend to contract all their capacity to utilities or other buyers in long-term agreements, and merchant generators, who sell to a variety of market participants in shorter deals and are generally more exposed to market prices. Others use the terms synonymously. Merchant generators and IPPs offer a number of services such as electricity (MWh), capacity (MW), and/or other ancillary services that may be sold to utilities, marketers, ISOs, or directly to end-use customers. Merchant generators and IPPs may build new generating stations or may acquire units from utilities selling off existing generation. Some merchant generators and IPPs evolved as unregulated subsidiaries of utility companies while others formed as independent companies. Examples of merchant generators and IPPs include AES, Calpine, Dynegy, Exelon Generation, and NRG Energy.

Transmission Companies

Transmission companies, or transcos, are independent owners of transmission facilities. They are investor-owned, and like IOUs they operate to make a profit for their shareholders. Because they are essential facilities they are regulated by FERC. They acquire their transmission lines either by buying them from formerly vertically integrated utilities that have decided to divest of transmission or by building new transmission facilities. When transcos build new facilities with financing based on transmission contracts with users (as opposed to financing based on inclusion of facilities in a regulated rate base), the facilities are called merchant transmission. Some market analysts envision that over time transcos will evolve to become a combination of transmission owner and system operator, but that has yet to occur in the United States. Examples of major transcos in the U.S. include American Transmission, ITC Holdings, and Cross Texas Transmission.

Independent System Operators (ISOs)/Regional Transmission Organizations (RTOs)

If competitive generation markets are to work effectively, generators must have non-discriminatory access to the transmission system to deliver their power to customers. The traditional structure in the U.S. is for transmission systems to be owned and operated by the utilities. This allows the utilities to control access to transmission since, under federal law, they are allowed to provide preference for service to native loads (their own customers). And because they also control the system operations function, they decide which units are dispatched in response to system needs.

Merchant generators and marketers argue that this creates an unfair playing field in the market. One solution is to create an Independent System Operator (ISO) or Regional Transmission Organization (RTO). An ISO/RTO does not own transmission but rather manages transmission owned by other entities (either utilities or transcos). The ISO/RTO handles all the system operations functions of scheduling generation, transmission, and reserves; acquiring other ancillary services; and managing the system in real time. In some cases, ISOs also facilitate day-ahead energy and forward capacity markets. ISOs/RTOs are non-profit organizations run by an independent board of directors that is not beholden to any one market participant or group of market participants. ISOs/RTOs in the United States are FERC-regulated entities with the exception of the ERCOT in Texas[3]. ISOs/RTOs in North America include the Alberta Electric System Operator, California ISO, CENACE, ERCOT, ISO New England, Midcontinent ISO, New York ISO, Independent Electric System Operator, PJM Interconnection, and SPP.

---

[3]Due to the configuration of transmission lines in Texas, power flows from the ERCOT control area generally don't cross state lines. Thus ERCOT has successfully maintained its status as state-regulated.

Electric Marketers

Marketers generally purchase electricity from generators and then resell it to utilities, end users, or other marketers. Successful marketers add value by saving generators and customers the trouble of finding each other, arranging for transmission and ancillary services, and sometimes assuming price or other marketplace risks. A number of generation companies have an electric marketing arm to handle marketing of their units' output, while others simply sell to independent marketing companies.

The role of the marketer is sometimes divided into two categories — the wholesale marketer and the retail marketer. Wholesale marketers buy power and resell it to utilities, other marketers, and very large industrial customers. Retail marketers also buy power but focus solely on resale to end-use customers. Since retail marketers usually have a lot more customers than wholesale marketers, their skills are focused on mass sales, customer service, product development, billing, credit and collections, and brand development. Wholesale marketers tend to focus more on risk management and direct sales. Examples of active electric marketers include BP, Direct Energy, Engie, Macquarie Group, and TXU Energy.

Financial Services Companies

Financial services companies provide risk management services associated with price risk and other risks that are inherent in the electricity industry. Electricity prices can be extremely volatile, and many market participants cannot handle the cash flow impacts of rapidly changing prices. Thus there is a market need for entities that can offer hedging products to lay off price risk. We will discuss this function further in Section Fourteen. Financial services companies active in the electric industry include J.P. Morgan, Bank of America, Goldman Sachs, and Deutsche Bank.

Transmission Owners

In markets where the system operations function has been moved to an ISO, the term transmission owner, or TO, is used to describe the entity that continues to own, maintain and, if necessary, expand the transmission system. The TO operates the transmission system under direction from the ISO and receives revenues from the ISO to cover the cost of ownership and expenses of operation. TOs may be transcos or they may be part of a utility company.

Utility Distribution Companies

As markets are restructured, many of the functions previously served by the monopoly utility are removed from the utility function and replaced by competitive companies. This can include generation, system operations, transmission, and retail sales of supply. The one remaining utility function is the distribution function. Thus in markets where generation and retail sales have been made competitive, the utility company becomes a UDC, or utility distribution company. The UDC is the monopoly provider of distribution services. This may also include providing supply to some customers — usually smaller customers who are not eligible for competitive services or larger customers who have chosen not to take service from a marketer. In other cases, regulation prohibits the UDC from offering supply services to any customer.

Load Serving Entities

In many regions, the term Load Serving Entity (LSE) is used to refer to any market participant that provides supply to end-use customers. This may be a UDC or it may be a retail marketer. Other terms used include energy services provider (ESP), retail electric company (REC), or retail energy provider (REP).

Energy Services Companies (ESCOs)

In competitive markets, ESCOs continue to provide an important market function. In addition to providing the services described in the vertically integrated market model, they may also assist larger end-use customers in evaluating the various market options and finding optimal solutions for acquiring supply and satisfying electric needs.

What you will learn:

- What an electric market structure is

- Goals of an electric market structure

- The electric market structures currently found in the U.S.

- How electric market structures function

- How different market structures address day-to-day system operations

- Future markets for distributed energy

9

SECTION NINE: ELECTRIC MARKET STRUCTURES

In the last few sections, we have learned about the necessary components of a functioning electric system. Supply resources must be built to provide energy and reserves, transmission lines must be built to move large amounts of power over long distances, and distribution systems must be built to distribute electricity safely to end-use consumers. And, of course, power system operations must tie it all together by dispatching resources to keep supply and demand in balance at all times.

The next issue we will address is how to structure a marketplace that allows all this to occur in a cost-effective and functioning manner. Capital must be attracted to allow for the construction of sufficient generation, transmission, and distribution. Markets must be designed to allow the various sectors to interact and to provide the various necessary reliability functions. And all the while the market structure must foster delivery of reliable and low-cost electricity to residential and business consumers.

Due to mixed efforts at market restructuring, we currently have varied electric market structures in place across the U.S. The story of how we got to where we are today — and where we may be going — is told in Section Twelve. Here we introduce five market structure models that are employed in the U.S. today and then discuss how each model addresses the necessary functions of electric generation, ancillary services, transmission access, and balancing supply and demand in real time.

What Is an Electric Market Structure?

An electric market structure is the set of rules and responsibilities that defines how market participants interact with each other to provide electricity to consumers. The key questions to defining a specific market structure are:

- Who is allowed to own generation and who will buy their output?
- Who will schedule generation, reserves, and transmission access in the day-ahead market, and who will manage the system in real time?

- Which customers, if any, will be allowed to buy supply directly from marketers or generators and which customers must buy from the distribution utility?

- How are business transactions performed to allow supply and system operations needs to be acquired by market participants?

The market structure that exists in any specific marketplace is determined by a combination of federal, state, and local legislation and/or federal and state regulatory decisions. Ultimately, an electric market structure should benefit consumers — specifically it should create reasonable prices, reliable service, and fairly predictable bills, and it should encourage innovation in services. The definition of a reasonable price, of course, is open to significant debate, but in general it means high enough to keep the supplier in business and able to invest in necessary infrastructure while low enough that residential consumers are not burdened with high electricity expenses and business consumers are not put at a disadvantage relative to other states and/or countries.

A key component of any market structure is the existence of — or lack of — competition. In general, there are three areas where competition has the potential to benefit consumers: generation of electricity, wholesale trading of electricity, and sales of electricity to retail customers. System operations and distribution are natural monopolies, at least in today's technological environment, and are not open to competition. We all pretty much agree that it does not make economic, environmental, or aesthetic sense to build duplicative distribution lines. And the very nature of system operations necessitates it be performed as a single centralized function. Transmission is partially in both camps. Construction of new transmission facilities can be open to competition since in the U.S.. FERC does not give exclusive service territories. But once lines are built, they are regulated as a monopoly. So in discussing different models for electric markets, we will focus on different levels of competition in generation, wholesale trading, and retail markets. We will also discuss the players that own and operate trans-

---

MARKET SECTORS THAT DEFINE MARKET STRUCTURE

Generation — The generation of electricity.

Transmission — The movement of electricity at high voltages, usually between generation and distribution systems.

Wholesale Trading — The trading of electricity between entities that are not end-use customers (such as generators, marketers and utilities).

System Operations — The operation of the generation and transmission grid to ensure supply matches loads at all times and that system reliability is maintained.

Distribution — The delivery of electricity (which may be owned by someone other than the distribution company) from the transmission system to the end-use customer.

Retail Sales — The sale of electricity and other value-added services to the end-use customer.

mission, distribution, and system operations and how these functions are restructured to support competition in the competitive sectors.

In this section we will discuss five basic market structures:

- Vertically integrated monopoly utility

- Single-buyer with competitive generation

- Wholesale/industrial competition

- Complete retail competition

- Hybrid retail competition with default utility supply

You should remember that these are only models, and actual markets may vary from them in the details.

Vertically Integrated Monopoly Utility Model

The vertically integrated monopoly utility model arose as electric service began in the late 1800s and survived unquestioned for close to 100 years. The concept behind this model is to treat generation, transmission, distribution, retail sales, and system opera-tions functions as an inte-grated whole — owned and performed by one monopoly entity or by closely aligned monopoly entities. In the United States, three different sub-models evolved within the vertically integrated model:

- The investor-owned utility (IOU)

- The municipal utility and public utility dis-trict (muni and PUD)

- The rural electric co-op (co-op)

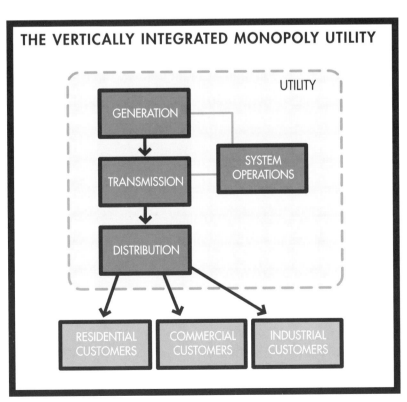

THE VERTICALLY INTEGRATED MONOPOLY UTILITY

In other countries federal or state/provincial ownership of utilities is common. The majority of U.S. customers are served by IOUs. Traditionally, IOUs have served their customers by running the generation, transmission, and distribution systems as a vertically integrated system designed to serve the needs of all end-use customers within their service territory. Sometimes IOUs trade with other IOUs to minimize supply costs and/or enhance reliability. In other cases this is done through power pools. But in general, under vertical integration the IOU owns everything and serves everyone within its territory.

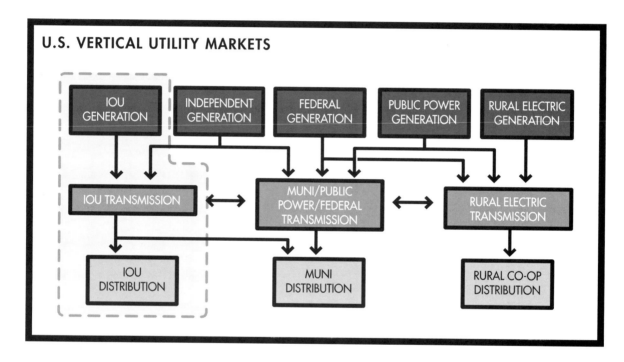

U.S. VERTICAL UTILITY MARKETS

9

In other areas, munis or rural co-ops have evolved as the distribution utility serving all customers within the utility's service area. Large munis operate much like IOUs with complete ownership of generation, transmission, and distribution. But smaller munis and co-ops do not have the necessary volume of customers to make it economical to own the complete vertical chain. These entities do own their distribution systems but either band together to jointly own generation and transmission in public power agencies or depend on federal generation agencies to supply the power to them.

Many areas of the United States still operate under the vertically integrated model. These include parts of the Southeast, the Northwest, the Rocky Mountain states, and the Southwest. Virtually all munis, PUDs, and co-ops still operate under the vertically integrated model with the exceptions noted above for sharing generation and transmission resources.

Single-buyer with Competitive Generation Model

The first movement toward introducing competition in an electric marketplace usually comes through the entry of competing electric generation providers. Without this, it is difficult to have competition in other sectors. Thus, the second market model is one in which the utility maintains the monopoly functions of transmission, distribution, and retail sales but in which non-utility generation is allowed to compete with utility generation. Initially in the U.S., only cogenerators were allowed to compete with utility generation, but in the 1990s changes in federal law allowed other non-utility generators to enter the marketplace.

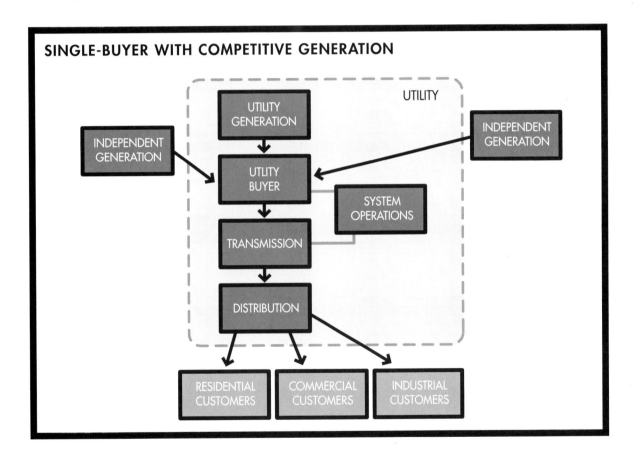

Under the single-buyer model, the utility company creates a supply purchasing group whose job is to competitively procure supply on behalf of all the utility's end-use customers. This power may be procured from the units owned by the utility as part of its regulated function or from merchant units owned by competitive entities. Under this model, system operations may be handled either by the utility or an Independent System Operator. Some wholesale trading outside of the utility may occur. But since

SECTION NINE: ELECTRIC MARKET STRUCTURES

the utility is the only buyer in the local market this happens only if a marketer is aggregating supply from generators and then selling it to the utility or if the marketer is moving power across the utility system into another market. The remainder of the market functions — transmission, distribution, and retail sales — continue to be the monopoly purview of the regulated utility.

Generally, the utility supply purchasing group makes its buying decisions based on reliability of supply and least cost. Since utility generation already has its capital and debt costs covered in customer rates, it does not need to capture these fixed costs in its prices and can offer lower bids. Thus, this model tends to result in independent generation selling into the utility only when existing utility generation is not sufficient to cover customer loads. If the utility is an IOU, it is necessary for the state regulatory body to create mechanisms to review its purchasing decisions to ensure they are in the interests of ratepayers and not the IOU's shareholders.

Many market participants will argue that the single-buyer model is really very limited competition. While generating units may be owned by entities other than the utility, their only source of revenue is sales to the utility. Thus there isn't much in the way of true competition. To get true competition, markets must allow producers and consumers to come together outside of the regulated monopoly.

Many states that otherwise subscribe to maintaining the utility monopolies have opened up their generation sectors to limited competition by implementing some form of the single-buyer model. A common implementation of this model in recent years has been the requirement that utilities needing new supply sources must consider power contracts with independent parties in addition to utility-constructed units when doing integrated resource planning. In some states using this model, new generation has been constructed by IPPs who then sign long-term (seven- to 10-year) supply agreements with the utility. Other states have implemented periodic auctions where the utility buyer acquires supply from the market using a centralized auction process.

Wholesale/Industrial Competition Model

Many observers of electric markets believe that the real benefits of competition are to be gained by allowing only large customers — the largest commercial and industrial customers — to competitively procure supply while the smaller customers continue to be served by the utility company under regulated rules. Their argument is that, at least initially, only large customers really care enough to get involved in competitive procurement and are sophisticated enough to look out for their own well being. This allows the competitive market to mature before deciding whether there are benefits to providing supply choice to smaller customers.

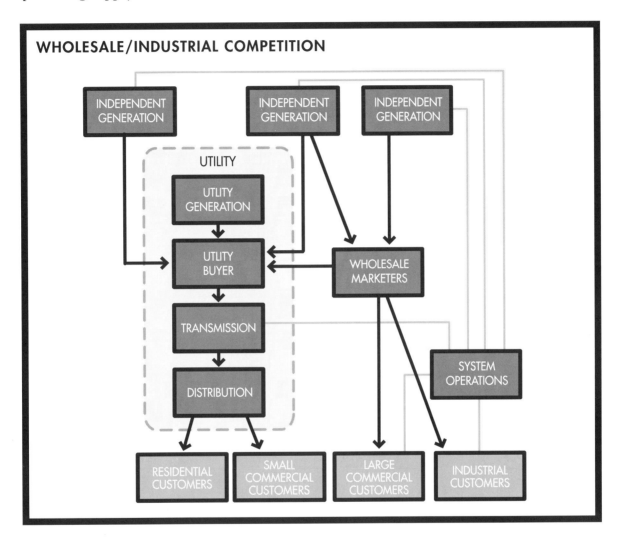

WHOLESALE/INDUSTRIAL COMPETITION

This philosophy leads us to the wholesale/industrial competition model in which large commercial and industrial customers purchase their electric supply directly from generators or wholesale marketers, but the utility maintains the single-buyer function for small commercial and residential customers. For this model to work, most regulators prefer an independent entity responsible for system operations. Since the system operator implements the rules that determine who gets access to transmission and whose units are ramped up or down in response to system needs, leaving the function within the utility could unfairly bias the markets. Thus an Independent System Operator (ISO) is created to handle the system operations functions. This market structure also creates the need for entities to match generators with end users, so the role of the marketer becomes important.

Transmission continues to be owned by the utility but is operated under the direction of the ISO[1]. The utility continues to own and operate the distribution system, providing distribution-only services to large customers and providing bundled distribution/supply services to smaller customers. The utility supply purchasing group acquires supply for all the smaller customers and, as in the previous model, has the option of obtaining supply from utility generation or through contracts with independent generators. In this model, however, a competitive wholesale market is likely to evolve. Because of this competition, smaller customers should see some benefits if it does result in lower wholesale prices since the utility buyer should have access to the lower-cost supplies.

Key issues for the regulator in this model include defining the arrangements the utility buyer is allowed to enter into to buy supply and determining how the cost of that supply is passed on to the customers who purchase it from the utility. Options for purchasing supply include bilateral contracts, spot purchases, and periodic auctions. Options for passing on costs include monthly or annual pass-through of costs or a rate cap that puts the utility at risk for costs above the cap.

Many of the states that have undergone electric deregulation initially implemented wholesale/industrial competition or some variation thereof. But as markets matured over time, most states have extended supply choice to small commercial and industrial customers.

Complete Retail Competition Model

Under complete retail competition the journey to a competitive market is complete. In this model, the utility has been completely removed from the supply function on both the generation and the retail sales side. The utility is now simply a transporter of electricity that provides the transmission and/or distribution infrastructure used by various market participants on an open-access basis. An ISO is required to perform the system operations functions in an unbiased manner. Wholesale and retail marketers acquire supply from generators and sell to each other as well as to end-use customers. Generators can sell directly to customers or to a marketer. Under this model, the regulators must create a mechanism for fulfilling the function of provider

---

[1] An alternative would be for independent transmission owners, or transcos, to take over the transmission systems. In theory, they could also take over the system operations functions and act much like interstate pipelines in today's natural gas marketplace. While we have seen some utilities sell off their transmission to regulated transmission companies, we have yet to see any examples of these companies also taking on the role of an ISO. This model is used in other countries such as Britain.

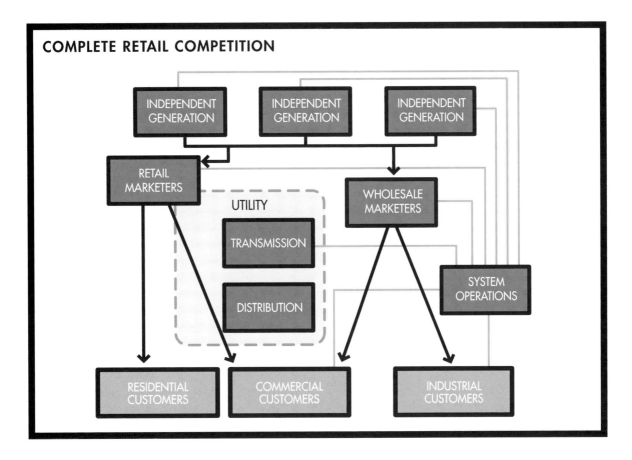

COMPLETE RETAIL COMPETITION

of last resort (POLR). The POLR serves customers who are unwilling or unable to contract with an electricity provider. This may be done by assigning customers to marketers on a pro-rata basis or by selecting a specific marketer to provide this service under regulated terms. As of 2019 only two states — Texas and Maine — have complete retail competition.

Hybrid Retail Competition Model

Although many states now allow choice of supplier to all customers, some still allow customers to choose to continue taking supply from the utility company under default regulated rates. Thus, while all customers have the option of choosing competitive supply, the utility maintains a procurement function for customers who do not choose a retail marketer. In the early years of this market model, most smaller customers chose to remain with the default utility supply while many of the larger commercial and industrial customers chose to purchase from the competitive market. However, as markets have matured an increasing percentage of smaller customers have chosen to

HYBRID RETAIL COMPETITION

purchase supply from competitive retail marketers. This model now represents the majority of states that have implemented deregulation.

Trading Arrangements

The five models discussed above answer all of the questions that define market structure with the exception of the last, which asks how business transactions are performed to allow supply and system operations needs to be acquired by the marketplace. As we move away from the vertically integrated utility model, we begin to take the supply and system operations functions from the utilities and turn them over to the marketplace. Given the physical complexity of the electrical system, these functions cannot be left to chance. Regulators and legislators must carefully devise market-based arrangements to ensure that participants can efficiently acquire generation and

THE MARKET MODELS					
Function	**Vertically Integrated Monopoly Utility**	**Single-buyer with Competitive Generation**	**Wholesale/Industrial Competition**	**Complete Retail Competition**	**Hybrid Retail Competition**
Providing generation	Utility	Utility and IPPs	Merchant generators and IPPs	Merchant generators and IPPs	Merchant generators and IPPs
Purchasing electricity	Utility	Utility	End users for large customers, utility for small customers	End users	End users and utility for default customers
Power plant scheduling and dispatch	Utility	Utility or ISO	ISO	ISO	ISO
Transmission scheduling	Utility	Utility or ISO	ISO	ISO	ISO
Running the day-ahead market	Not applicable	ISO or not applicable	ISO	ISO	ISO
Ensuring supply and demand are balanced in real time	Utility	Utility or ISO	ISO	ISO	ISO
Managing distribution functions	Utility	Utility	Utility	Utility	Utility
Providing supply to end users	Utility	Utility	Utility for small customers, marketers or generators for large customers	Marketers or generators	Marketers, generators, or utility
Long-term planning	Utility	Utility	Utility for small customers, market for large customers, and ISO for both	Market and ISO	Market, ISO, and utility

that system operations functions continue to be provided. These rules are called trading arrangements.

Trading arrangements answer the following questions:

- How do buyers arrange for electric supply in forward markets?

- How do buyers arrange for electric supply in day-ahead markets?

- How do buyers arrange for ancillary services?

- How do market participants receive access to the transmission system?

- How do markets ensure sufficient capacity over the long term?

The three basic ways of structuring trading arrangements are wheeling, decentralized, and integrated. Each is discussed in detail below.

TRADING ARRANGEMENTS

- Forward and day-ahead energy markets

- Generation scheduling and dispatch

- Ancillary services scheduling and dispatch

- Transmission access

- Managing imbalances in real time

- Real-time energy markets

- Long-term capacity

Wheeling

Trading arrangements under wheeling are applicable only to the vertically integrated utility and the single-buyer models. Under the wheeling method, each utility schedules its own generation plus any purchased power in the day ahead based on the utility's load forecast. Ancillary services are scheduled by the utility from its own generation or are acquired by the utility from nearby utilities or IPPs through bilateral agreements (a bilateral agreement is simply a private contract between two parties). Generation, purchased power, and ancillary services are scheduled in an integrated manner to provide the lowest-cost service subject to transmission and other constraints.

Imbalances between scheduled generation and loads in real time are managed by the utility's system operator who simply ramps up or down utility-owned or contracted units that the operator has under full control. The transmission system is made available for use by parties who wish to wheel power (i.e. move the power across the utility transmission system for delivery to a neighboring utility) on an open-access basis but only to the extent that wheeling transactions do not impact the utility's service to its own customers (native load). Transmission services and any necessary related ancillary services are made available to the wheeling parties under regulated tariff rates. Long-term capacity adequacy is ensured by utilities with oversight by regulators. The wheeling model is currently used in areas where there is no ISO.

Decentralized

The decentralized method is one of two ways of structuring trading arrangements that are applicable to competitive markets with independent generators, an ISO, and end users able to buy directly from marketers. The decentralized model moves as far away from the concept of a centralized market as is possible. An ISO is still required to handle scheduling, acquisition of ancillary services, access to transmission, and management of the system in real time. But in this model, the ISO is seen mostly as a scheduler and an arbiter of free markets. For electricity bought and sold for future periods (forward markets), all contracts are simply bilateral agreements between generators and end users or entities that supply end users (Load Serving Entities or LSEs). In some markets, a separate entity called a Power Exchange (PX) is created to facilitate trading. To obtain access to transmission, entities wishing to move power (known as scheduling coordinators) submit to the ISO balanced schedules that match specific supply to specific loads for each hour. Upon receiving the schedules for a specific hour, the ISO runs its power flow model to determine whether all requested schedules are feasible. If not, transmission congestion exists and access to transmission is allocated by an auction methodology. Market participants bid for the rights to use certain paths (or offer how much they would need to be paid to change their schedules to relieve the congestion), and transmission access is granted to those willing to pay the most. The market clearing price (i.e., the lowest accepted price bid for access to the path) is paid by all users of the path in a transmission congestion charge.

Necessary ancillary services, in amounts that meet reliability criteria, are either self-supplied by each scheduling coordinator or are acquired from the market by the ISO on behalf of the customers. Customers who do not supply their own ancillary services pay their pro-rata share of ancillary services costs to the ISO in an ancillary services charge. The ISO acquires ancillary services through auctions for each service (i.e. spinning reserves, non-spinning reserves, etc.). Any generator in the marketplace that has not committed its generation in a bilateral contract can bid into the auction. The ISO stacks the bids and takes the lowest that will satisfy the needed capacity amount. All successful bidders are then paid the market clearing price (i.e., the highest bid accepted in a specific auction). Lastly, the ISO creates a stack of units available to provide real-time balancing energy (units that are willing to either ramp up or down in real time). This stack comes from successful ancillary service bidders plus additional units with uncommitted capacity that offer energy into the real-time market. The ISO then manages the system in real time by following its bid stack to increase or decrease supply in response to demand. Scheduling coordinators who create an imbalance in real time (meaning they either have more or less generation than they do demand on the system among their generator/customer pool) are charged/paid an after-the-fact imbalance price that is based on the prices paid to the units ramped up or down in real time. Under this model there is no provision to ensure long-term capacity adequacy — it is assumed markets will provide the right amount.

As you can probably see, the decentralized method gets very complex very quickly. For each hour of the day, ISOs are running numerous auctions for transmission congestion, ancillary services, and real-time stacks. Market uncertainly abounds as costs for ancillary services, transmission access, and real-time energy change hourly, often in unpredictable ways. And costs for real-time imbalances are not even known until after the fact. The existence of complexity creates numerous opportunities for market participants to find market weaknesses that can be exploited. ISOs are completely dependent on the marketplace to provide necessary ancillary services and imbalance energy. If the supply in any market becomes constrained, prices can skyrocket and the ISO has no means of optimizing solutions by moving generation from one market to the other. Many observers believe that one of the market design issues that led to the California crisis was the use of the decentralized model. The multiple and complex auctions allowed marketers to "arbitrage" between markets and find opportunities for excess profits. In such a situation, it is difficult for an ISO to craft and implement all the necessary rules to prevent these types of activities. In the U.S., the two large ISOs that initially used the decentralized method (California and Texas) have transitioned to the integrated model in recent years. But the decentralized model continues to be used in many European markets.

Integrated

The integrated method is the second methodology that can be applied to competitive markets. This method attempts to strike a balance between the complexity of the decentralized method and the lack of competition in the wheeling method. It recognizes the benefits of centralized markets and generation dispatch while creating ways for competition to be taken into account in the operation of centralized markets.

Under the integrated method, the historical concept of a power pool is modified into the concept of an ISO that operates day-ahead energy markets as well as other system operations functions. The ISO is responsible for scheduling units in the day ahead, allocating transmission, scheduling reserves, and balancing supply and demand in real time. Rather than running each of these as a separate and distinct market, as is done in the decentralized method, the ISO operates all the markets in one integrated, optimized fashion.

Basically, the ISO uses the old system operations model from the vertically integrated utility days, which created optimized schedules subject to system constraints. But it replaces the model cost inputs (marginal cost in the utility days) with bids placed by market participants. Owners of units bid for what they wish to be paid to operate during a given hour and also what they wish to be paid to provide reserves. Suppliers of

FUNCTIONS WITHIN THE THREE TRADING ARRANGEMENTS MODELS

Function	Wheeling	Decentralized	Integrated
Transmission scheduling	Done by utility as adjunct to scheduling for its own customers	Done by ISO, congestion management done by auction	Done by ISO as part of optimization model
Generation reserves scheduling (ancillary services)	Done by utility, wheeling customers are charged a regulated price for the service	Done by ISO in multiple auctions	Done by ISO as part of optimization model
Operating day-ahead spot market	Done by utility or power pool run by utilities	Done by PX in some regions, in others it is handled in the bilateral market	Done by ISO as part of optimization model
Dispatching balancing units in real time	Done by utility	Done by ISO, units available determined by auction	Done by ISO, units available determined by optimization
Setting market price for day-ahead market	Limited market, price is set by bilateral wholesale transactions or by power pool	Can be done by ISO through bilateral transactions or by an independent power exchange	Done by ISO as part of optimization
Setting market price for balancing market	Managed internally by utility	Done by ISO based on bid price of last unit dispatched	Done by ISO as part of optimization

loads bid for what they are willing to pay to receive power during a given hour. Typically the ISO runs a day-ahead market that matches supply to demand given the price bids, then minimizes overall system costs subject to constraints by creating a system schedule. If there are constraints on the transmission system, the ISO determines which units will be dispatched at what levels based on their bids. Locational prices are created and users of constrained transmission paths pay a congestion charge based on the difference in prices between the two locations (this is called locational marginal pricing). In real time, the ISO manages imbalances through a real-time market that ramps units up or down based on bid price. Under this model the ISO may also run a short- or long-term capacity market to ensure sufficient generation is built.

The Current Status of Market Structures and Trading Arrangements

As you have learned, the U.S. currently has highly fragmented electric markets. Variations of the market models and trading arrangements methodologies are used in various states. This fragmentation is due to the way electricity is regulated — i.e., responsibility is split between states and the federal government. This makes it very difficult to create uniform markets across the U.S. as different states have different goals and different ideas about how to reach them. The fragmented markets also make it more costly for energy companies to do business across state lines or move electricity from one region to the next, and they also impede development of our electric infrastructure.

The mid-2010s saw the expansion of ISO markets as a means of addressing some of these difficulties. This included Entergy, CLECO, and other utilities from the Southeast joining MISO; SPP adding utilities from parts of six states in the upper Great Plains region; and numerous Western utilities choosing to participate in the CAISO real-time market via the newly created Energy Imbalance Market. Growth of integrated ISO markets also extended to Mexico with the creation of the country-wide CENACE ISO.

Markets for Distributed Energy

In the mid-2010s growth of distributed energy resources (DERs) including distributed generation such as rooftop solar, economic demand response, and distributed storage raised the issue of whether markets are needed for distributed resources. Initially, most DERs were simply treated as negative load, meaning that they reduced the amount of energy that customers used and thus reduced their electric bill. But as DERs grow and distributed power is put back onto the grid, new distributed market structures will be needed. Some states are already addressing the issue by requiring electric distribution utilities to create new market mechanisms. As of 2019, New York is leading the way with its Reforming the Energy Vision (REV) proceeding that will result in utilities transforming to become Distribution System Platform Providers with a mandate to facilitate distributed markets. Similar concepts are being implemented in Hawaii. And across the U.S., ISOs are developing new market rules that will facilitate participation of aggregated DERs in wholesale markets. It is likely this trend will grow in future years.

What you will learn:

- Why the electric industry is regulated

- The goals of regulators

- The historical basis for regulation

- Who regulates what

- How regulators establish rates and rules

- The various types of regulatory proceedings

- What tariffs are

- The rate case process

- What incentive regulation is and how it works

- How regulation works for monopoly utilities

- How regulation works for wholesale sales

10

10

SECTION TEN: REGULATION IN THE ELECTRIC INDUSTRY

It is impossible to understand the electric marketplace without a comprehensive understanding of the role of regulation. Regulation exists to ensure that customers of electric utilities and other service providers are protected from a lack of competition. To protect the public interest, regulation defines the services that regulated market participants can offer, sets rates to be charged for those services, prescribes accounting systems to track costs associated with them, enforces safety and reliability standards, approves construction of major new projects built by regulated entities, monitors market behaviors of industry participants, and in some cases establishes rules to foster public policy goals.

As the electric marketplace evolves, traditional concepts of regulation are also evolving. This evolution has hardly been uniform. Some states have moved forward with significant restructuring of regulatory-defined market structures while others have refused to venture beyond the traditional models. Thus an understanding of regulation at both the national and local levels, as well as an understanding of how regulation may be evolving, is critical to success in an electric marketplace that can be both highly regulated and highly competitive. In this section we will explore who the national, state, and local regulators are and how they determine the rules and rates for the services they regulate.

Why Regulate the Electric Industry?

The electric industry must be regulated due to the existence of monopolies. A monopoly is a business situation in which a corporation — through market power or a government-granted franchise — is either the only company conducting business in a given industry or the sole source of a specific commodity or service. A "natural monopoly" occurs in an industry where characteristics of the industry tend to result in monopolies evolving. A good example is the electric utility industry where a proportionately large capital investment is required to produce a single unit of output and where large operators can provide goods or services at a lower average cost than can small operators. Both of these conditions occurred in the electric industry in the early

1900s. Thus what began as a competitive industry quickly evolved into a market with few competitors. The resulting extreme market power of the survivors created the potential for excessive profits and unfair favoritism to certain customers. This in turn created the need for government oversight of electric services.

The relationship between regulators and utilities is often described as the "regulatory compact." This means that in return for government regulators granting exclusive service territories and setting rates in a manner that provides an opportunity for a reasonable return on investment, investor-owned public utilities submit their operations to full regulation. In this section we will discuss the history of regulation and then look at how current market restructuring requires modification of the traditional regulatory compact for certain electric industry sectors.

The Goals of Regulators

Regulators generally seek to:

- Minimize costs to consumers and provide relatively stable rates
- Maintain a fair playing field by not allowing undue discrimination
- Ensure reliable service
- Maximize the efficiency of resource use
- Minimize negative environmental impacts
- Ensure safety
- Encourage innovation in services to customers
- Foster societal and public policy goals such as clean energy development, economic development, or national security

Any given regulatory body may choose to focus on some or all of these goals. It should be remembered that in the end regulators are political in nature, and their attention to specific goals is driven by the political realities at any given period in time.

The Historical Basis for Regulation

State Regulation

In the late 1800s, the utility industry developed in an environment of open competition. Most cities and states believed that competition between utilities kept prices down, and it was not uncommon to find cities with numerous utilities operating in open competition. In fact, competition became so fierce that price wars were common, often leading to the demise of all but one utility, which could then take advantage of the lack of competition by raising customers' rates exorbitantly! As the electricity market evolved it became clear that its capital-intensive nature resulted in market inefficiencies (too much money spent on duplicative facilities) and allowed well-financed companies to push less successful ones out of the market.

To address this issue, state and local governments saw two options: municipal ownership of utilities or regulation of those that remained owned by shareholders. Between 1896 and 1906, the number of municipal utility systems more than tripled. This led investors who had created new shareholder-owned utilities to realize that they were in risk of losing the market to government entities. In 1907 the largest utility association (the National Electric Light Association) joined with the National Civic Federation (a turn-of-the-century big business advocacy group) in favor of state regulation of electric companies. Subsequently the states of Massachusetts, New York, and Wisconsin created the first state regulatory agencies. By 1916, 33 states had created regulatory agencies to oversee electric utilities. By this time, the model of a vertically integrated utility owning generation, transmission, and distribution facilities and providing service in a specific franchise area under state or local regulation was well entrenched.

Federal Regulation

On the federal level, regulation was emerging as well. In the industry's early years, Congress allowed utilities to build and operate dams without regulation. But in 1905, the federal government began to license dams and charge fees for their construction. In 1920, the Federal Water Power Act created the Federal Power Commission (the predecessor of today's FERC) whose role was to regulate rates, financing, and services of companies licensed to operate dams.

By the late 1920s, the government grew concerned with the emerging large utility holding companies. These holding companies owned multiple local utility operating companies through a complex web of subsidiaries. By 1929, seven utility holding companies controlled 60% of the power in the U.S. Although the local utilities were regulated, nobody was responsible for oversight of the holding companies. Concerns about the potential for market power and financial shenanigans became so widespread that the federal government felt compelled to act. It took initial action with construction of federal power projects that, rather than selling their output to IOUs, made the power available to public power agencies on a preference basis. This encouraged public power as competition to the IOUs.

Then in 1935 Congress enacted two new laws. The Public Utility Holding Company Act (PUHCA) required interstate utility holding companies to register with the Securities and Exchange Commission (SEC) and to follow specific rules. PUHCA also broke up holding company systems that were not contiguous and prevented utilities from investing in non-utility businesses. The Federal Power Act exerted federal control over electric sales across state lines and expanded the authority of the Federal Power Commission to include regulation of such sales. Thus large utilities had two tiers of regulation — operations for service to their own customers were regulated by state commissions while sales to neighboring utilities were subject to federal jurisdiction. Although the Federal Power Act referenced sales across state lines, future court decisions extended this jurisdiction to all sales between utilities using transmission lines, since physically once electricity is on the transmission line it is impossible to say whether it stays within a state or not[1]. PUHCA was highly effective in breaking apart holding companies — between 1935 and 1950, 759 utilities were separated from holding companies, and between 1938 and 1958 the number of registered holding companies declined from 216 to 18[2].

Federal involvement in the utility industry was further strengthened by:

- The Atomic Energy Act in 1946, which established the Atomic Energy Agency (the forerunner of today's Nuclear Regulatory Commission) and gave it regulatory oversight of nuclear generation. In later amendments it required open-access transmission by utilities licensing nuclear plants.

- The passage of major environmental laws beginning with the National Environmental Policy Act of 1969 and including the Clear Air Act of 1970.

- The Public Utilities Regulatory Policies Act of 1978 (PURPA) and the National Energy Policy Act of 1992, which ended the utility monopoly on generation and gave FERC authority to require utilities to allow third parties to move electricity across utility transmission lines.

- Various other FERC actions in the late 1990s to further its role in regulation of restructured competitive wholesale electric markets.

---

[1]Certain sales in Texas have operated under state regulation due to the fact that Texas has configured its transmission grid so that it can be argued that electricity cannot leave the portion of the state covered by the ERCOT ISO.

[2]PUHCA was repealed by the Energy Policy Act of 2005.

- The Energy Policy Act of 2005, which gave FERC jurisdiction over electric reliability and clarified FERC's authority to penalize participants that manipulate markets.

- Supreme Court decisions in 2016 that supported FERC's authority to set pricing for distributed resources participating in wholesale markets and clarified that states cannot create rules that intrude on FERC's authority over interstate wholesale rates.

We will discuss many of the more recent federal actions in Section Twelve when we consider market restructuring.

Who Regulates What?

Regulation of the electric marketplace is split between federal, state, and local jurisdictions. For vertically integrated utilities, services including generation, transmission, and distribution on behalf of the utilities' own customers are exempted from federal jurisdiction. These activities are regulated by:

- The state commissions for IOUs.

- The local governmental entity for municipal utilities in most states (13 states regulate some aspects of municipal utilities including rates).

- The co-op board for rural electric co-ops in most states (19 states regulate some aspects of co-ops including rates).

In states where restructuring has broken up the vertical utility, the IOU's utility distribution function and any remaining regulated supply options remain under the jurisdiction of the state commissions. In these states, most sales of electricity to end users by marketers are only lightly regulated, but often the states create a minimal set of rules by which the marketers must abide.

Once utilities begin selling power to other parties besides their own end-use customers, federal jurisdiction is applicable for those specific transactions (although state jurisdiction continues to apply to vertically integrated activities associated with service to the utilities' own customers). Thus the FERC regulates power sales between utilities and other wholesale entities (other utilities and marketers) and transmission services not on behalf of a utility's end-use customers (commonly called wheeling services). This jurisdiction applies not only to wholesale sales and transmission service activities of IOUs but of munis and co-ops as well[3]. FERC also regulates sales by any

---

[3]One exception is that sales of power by co-op generation and transmission companies to co-op distribution companies are not subject to FERC jurisdiction.

power plants and services by any transmission lines not operated as part of a vertical utility. So merchant power plants and transcos are subject to FERC, not state jurisdiction. This applies even to utility companies that own generation in subsidiaries separate from the UDC and sell the output to their own UDC. In short, if the service is not part of unified vertical utility, it is subject to FERC jurisdiction. This also applies to ISOs, even if they operate only in one state (with the exception of Texas).

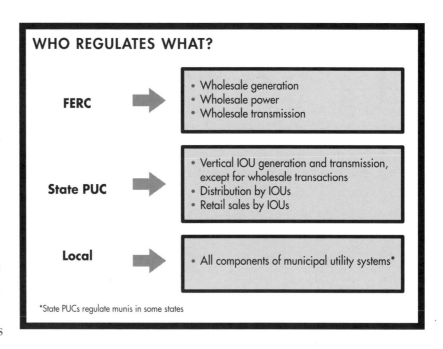

Power plant siting is subject to state jurisdiction, while power plant environmental regulations are federally and state mandated. Many environmental regulations are enforced by the Environmental Protection Agency (EPA) while others are enforced by state agencies. Operation of nuclear power plants is federally regulated by the Nuclear Regulatory Commission.

The Regulatory Process

Rates and rules are established through regulatory proceedings that are designed to give all interested parties a fair opportunity to state their opinions and present supporting facts. Regulatory proceedings include:

- Rulemakings — Proceedings held to establish new rules by which regulated entities conduct business.

- Rate cases — Proceedings that establish the rates a utility can charge for its services.

- Certificate cases — Proceedings that approve construction of new facilities.

- Complaint cases — Proceedings that evaluate complaints filed against utilities.

Following is a discussion of the general process used by regulators to set rates and rules for regulated services. Each regulator, however, may define this process in its own fashion.

The Initial Filing

A proceeding is typically initiated by a filing from a regulated entity (for rate cases and certificate cases) or by a market participant (for complaint cases). The documents filed are reviewed by the commission staff and a formal process begins. Rulemakings are a bit different. They apply when a major restructuring or change in regulation is contemplated, and in this case the regulatory agency takes the lead. Thus they are initiated by the regulator, who prepares and publishes a proposed rulemaking that describes how the regulator suggests changing market rules and/or ratemaking.

Preliminary Procedures

Usually an administrative law judge (ALJ) or one of the commissioners is assigned responsibility for steering the case through the regulatory process. This person is charged with conducting the public hearings and with preparing a recommended decision for the full commission to consider. Prior to the start of the proceeding, a pre-hearing conference is often scheduled that allows any interested party to make an appearance and state the extent to which it will participate in the hearings. The party must identify the issues it will raise and is asked to state whether it will file briefs, submit evidence, and/or cross-examine witnesses. These parties are then deemed intervenors in the case and secure certain participatory rights in the proceeding. Following the pre-hearing conference, the ALJ or assigned commissioner sets a date for hearings.

Hearings

Hearings are held to ensure the commission is aware of all important evidence relating to issues being considered. This is important because the commission must issue its decision solely based on the oral and written evidence presented in the case (the evidentiary record). Prior to hearings, the intervenors generally file written documents (opening briefs) stating their position on the issues. Hearings are then held to provide evidence in support of the various parties' positions. Evidence may be entered through written documents (exhibits) or through written or oral testimony by witnesses. Witnesses are subject to cross-examination and all testimony is given under oath. Some bodies, such as FERC, depend mostly on paper hearings and rarely hold hearings with witnesses. In some cases, such hearings are replaced with technical conferences where parties have an opportunity to state their positions but formal cross-examination is not used. At the conclusion of testimony, interested parties usually have another opportunity to file a written statement arguing their position (closing briefs), and then all parties have the opportunity to respond to each other's closing briefs (reply briefs). All closing and reply briefs are supposed to be based solely on the factual evidence presented in the hearings, and no new evidence can be introduced at this point in the proceeding. Although this sounds like a very clearly defined process, it should be noted that commissions have wide latitude in how they run hearings and politics can often play a significant role in what occurs.

The Draft Decision

Following the hearings, the ALJ or commissioner issues a draft decision, which is subsequently reviewed by the entire commission. Parties may file written comments on the draft decision for consideration by the full commission. Based on these comments, the ALJ or presiding commissioner may revise his or her draft decision before submitting it to the full commission as the suggested action. The draft decision is by no means final and represents only the opinion (educated, we hope) of the ALJ or assigned commissioner. The commission as a whole decides on whether the draft decision or an alternative point of view will be final.

The Final Decision

After all comments have been filed, the full commission considers the draft decision at a hearing conference. Changes to the draft decision may be made by the commissioners, and occasionally two versions of a decision will be considered simultaneously. In this case, the decision different from the draft decision is called an "alternate decision." A decision becomes law when a majority of the commissioners vote in support of it. At that point, it is called a final decision.

Review of Decisions

Any final decision is subject to review by the commission that issued it. Parties may request review either through a Petition for Modification or a Request for Rehearing. Petitions for Modification apply when a party believes that a decision fails to reflect the factual evidence presented in the evidentiary record. A Request for Rehearing applies when facts have changed since the evidentiary record was completed. If the commission denies review, or chooses to uphold the decision after review, the requesting party may ask the state (or U.S., depending on jurisdiction) courts to review the decision.

Tariffs

Tariffs are public documents, written by regulated entities and approved by the regulatory commission, that detail rates, rules, service territories, and terms of service. Tariffs are supposed to be written in accordance with the final decision of the regulatory body. Since decisions are often open to interpretation, tariffs must be approved by the regulatory body before they are legal. In general, tariffs include the following:

- A preliminary statement that describes the utility's terms of service and service territory and sets forth the accounts and adjustment mechanisms used in revenue accounting.

- Rate schedules that define rates and other terms of service for specific classes of customers.

- Rules that detail terms and conditions for service not described in rate schedules.

- Sample forms, including all standard form contracts, approved contract deviations, and other standard forms used in day-to-day business.

Tariffs that have been approved by a regulatory commission are binding legal documents that represent the contract between the regulated entity and its customers. A regulated entity cannot change its tariffs or fail to follow any provision in its tariffs in any way without approval from the regulatory agency. Copies of entities' tariffs can usually be found on the company's website.

Setting Rates through a Traditional Rate Case

A prime example of the regulatory process is ratemaking. One of the most important functions of the regulator is to set rates for monopoly services. The general concept of ratemaking is that monopoly entities are entitled to charge rates that will allow them to cover their costs of service plus a reasonable rate of return (or profit) on capital invested by shareholders to build the necessary facilities to provide safe and reliable service to ratepayers. The process of setting rates requires determining a revenue requirement that includes all the revenue the utility needs to collect to cover costs and make a reasonable return, and then translating that revenue requirement into specific rates for specific customers. This process is outlined below.

Determining the Authorized Rate of Return

The first step in the ratemaking process is a determination of the utility's authorized rate of return. This is set by the regulatory commission, sometimes as part of the rate case and other times in a separate proceeding called a cost of capital proceeding. The regulators look at the current investment marketplace and determine how much return investors must be offered to ensure they invest in utility stocks or debt as opposed to other investment opportunities. Separate rates of return will be set for utility debt and for equity, which is the money invested by stockholders. The two rates, weighted by the amount of debt and the amount of equity, are used to determine the overall authorized rate of return.

Forecasting Usage

The second step is to forecast how much electricity customers will need over the rate case period. This information is important because it will determine the amount of capital and expense dollars that will be required to provide reliable service and the revenue that the utility will collect. Forecasts are made using historical usage data, expected growth or decline in population, and business activities and other societal trends. The forecast will be broken down by customer class so that costs and revenues can be determined on a per-class basis.

Determining a Revenue Requirement

A revenue requirement is defined as the total amount of money a utility must collect from customers to pay all its costs, including its return on investment. A utility's revenue requirement is determined by forecasting expenses (operating and maintenance, administrative and generation, commodity costs, fuel costs for power generation, and taxes other than income taxes), depreciation, and income taxes for a rate cycle, and then adding to that the return on rate base plus any amounts (positive or negative) outstanding in balancing accounts. The rate base is the depreciated value of all the capital facilities the utility has constructed in order to provide services to its customers. The return on equity multiplied by the rate base multiplied by the percentage financed through shareholder investment is the primary component of profit for a monopoly utility.

A balancing account is an accounting mechanism that keeps track of the difference between projected expenses and actual expenses or projected revenues and actual revenues. Any differences covered by the balancing account are added to or subtracted from future revenue requirements, thus insulating the utility and its customers from risks of revenue deviations. Typical portions of the revenue requirement covered by balancing accounts include fuel costs and revenue fluctuations due to energy use that differs from the forecast for utilities with revenue decoupling (see page 195).

> **DETERMINING A REVENUE REQUIREMENT**
>
> Expenses
> +
> Depreciation
> +
> Income Taxes
> +
> Rate Base x Authorized Rate of Return
> +/—
> Balancing Account Adjustment

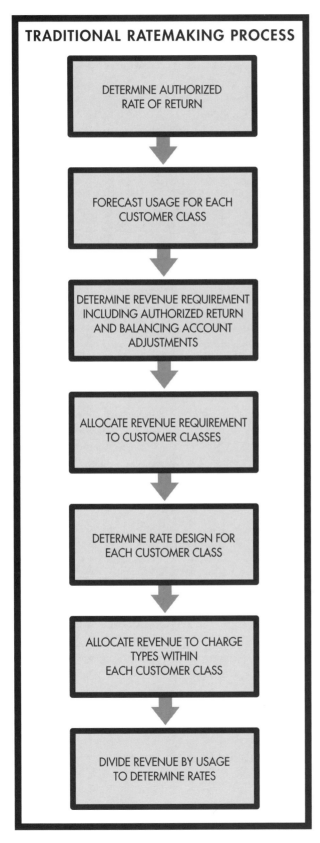

TRADITIONAL RATEMAKING PROCESS

DETERMINE AUTHORIZED
RATE OF RETURN

FORECAST USAGE FOR EACH
CUSTOMER CLASS

DETERMINE REVENUE REQUIREMENT
INCLUDING AUTHORIZED RETURN
AND BALANCING ACCOUNT
ADJUSTMENTS

ALLOCATE REVENUE REQUIREMENT
TO CUSTOMER CLASSES

DETERMINE RATE DESIGN FOR
EACH CUSTOMER CLASS

ALLOCATE REVENUE TO CHARGE
TYPES WITHIN
EACH CUSTOMER CLASS

DIVIDE REVENUE BY USAGE
TO DETERMINE RATES

Allocating Revenue to Customer Classes

Once an overall revenue requirement for a utility service is established, it must then be determined what portion will be paid by each class of customer. This process is called revenue allocation. Various allocation methods are used in different situations. The most simple method (equal cents per kWh) allocates costs based on usage. While simple, this approach is not necessarily an accurate way of assigning costs. Since many of the costs of an electric system are fixed, actual costs caused by customers are more likely to be based on the maximum demand that a customer puts on the system and not on the amount of kWh used. Thus a more common — though more complex — method is to allocate costs based on the estimated cost of service to each customer category (cost-of-service). This allocation can take into account demand-based costs as well as usage-based costs. An even more complex method (equal proportionate marginal costs or EPMC) allocates costs based on the marginal cost of serving each customer category. The marginal cost methodology looks at the cost of serving one additional increment in each class rather than using the average cost as is done in the cost-of-service methodology. Actual determination of revenue allocation can be complex and is commonly one of the most highly contested issues in regulatory proceedings.

Determining Rate Design

Once a revenue requirement has been determined and allocated to the various customer classes, the rates that each customer class will pay are determined in the rate design phase of the proceeding. But before actual rates can be set, the rate structure must be determined. Rates are structured in any number of ways, but typically they are divided into three distinct components:

- Customer charges — A per-customer charge independent of usage.

- Demand charges — These charges are based on the maximum demand (kW) placed on the system during a specified period of time and are usually applied only to larger customers (due to the prohibitive cost of metering demand for small customers).

- Usage charges — These charges depend on actual usage (kWh) during a period of time. For many customers the rates used to calculate usage charges stay the same no matter when the energy is used. For larger customers, however, it is common to charge a different rate for different periods of the day. This methodology is called time-of-use rates. In some cases rates may also differ by season (i.e., summer vs. winter rates).

During the rate design process, the method of allocating revenue between the different types of rate charges is also determined.

Allocating Revenue to Charge Types

Once the rate structure is set, another allocation must occur. This is the allocation within a customer class that determines how much revenue will be applied to customer charges, demand charges, and usage charges. Once this has been done, we now know how much revenue the utility is expected to collect from each charge type within each customer class.

Determining the Rate

Finally, the rates for each customer type are calculated by dividing the allocated revenue by the appropriate forecasted factor. For instance, a residential customer class that is allocated $1 million per month to customer charges and has 100,000 customers forecasted would have a monthly customer charge of $1 million divided by 100,000 customers, which equals $10 per customer per month.

Incentive Regulation

The process presented above is often called cost-of-service ratemaking. One complaint about this method is that in the absence of competition, utilities may not have incentive to keep costs down. The only incentive is the fear that the regulator may disallow expenses or capital spending that are deemed excessive. When regulators do disallow expenses, utilities feel unfairly penalized (since it is always easy to second guess a cost after the fact). This conundrum has led some regulators to move to incentive regulation. Incentive regulation is designed to avoid after-the-fact reasonableness reviews while aligning shareholder and ratepayer interests by allowing both sides to benefit from successful performance by the utility. Examples of incentive regulation include performance-based, benchmarking, and rate caps, each of which is described in more detail below.

Performance-based

Performance-based regulation compares the utility's performance to a specific metric. An example is the procurement of gas supply for resale to a utility's customers. The utility's cost of buying gas would be compared with a market index for gas prices in the utility's area. If the utility's cost is lower than the market index, the utility's shareholders and ratepayers split the savings. Conversely, if the utility's cost of gas is higher, shareholders and ratepayers split the increased cost. This, of course, provides strong incentive for the utility to pay close attention to its gas purchasing strategies. Other examples of performance-based regulation might include incentives/penalties for achieving a certain level of customer satisfaction or maintaining a certain level of service without any outages, attaining safety goals, and reducing environmental impacts.

As of 2019, numerous regulators have implemented or are in the process of implementing performance-based rates (PBR) including the states of Hawaii, Illinois, and New York as well as all of the United Kingdom.

Benchmarking

Benchmarking regulation sets rates in the first year of a rate cycle using traditional methods. For future years, rates are set by a formula that increases them based on an appropriate inflation index and then reduces them based on a regulatory-determined productivity factor that the utility is expected to achieve. This is often called X-Y regulation where the factor X represents inflationary increases and factor Y represents productivity-based decreases. This encourages the utility to go out and find ways to enhance productivity and to keep costs below inflation since any difference between actual costs and revenues collected in rates is a 100% cost/benefit to shareholders.

Rate Caps

Under rate cap methodology, fixed rates are set by the regulator for a period of years. Any variation between actual costs and revenue collected under the capped rates is a 100% cost/benefit to shareholders.

Service Standards

To ensure that utilities do not let service quality decline in the interest of achieving incentive revenue, regulators often create specific measurable service standards. Failure to achieve these standards results in shareholder penalties.

Market-based Rates

In cases where market forces are strong enough to prevent potential monopoly abuses, regulators have allowed regulated entities to charge market-based rates. This is common in the wholesale marketplace where generators and marketers that do not have a large enough market share to control markets are allowed to charge market-based rates. This type of regulation is the fundamental principle that underlies competitive electric markets created by market restructuring. To charge market-based rates, generators or marketers selling power in the wholesale market must receive a certificate from FERC authorizing them to do so. But first they must demonstrate a lack of market power. FERC retains the right to implement rate caps and/or penalties at any point should these entities be observed exerting market power.

State and Federal Rate Methodologies

As noted above, the states are responsible for regulating the activities of vertically integrated investor-owned utilities as well as investor-owned utility distribution companies. The state commissions are generally referred to as the Public Utility Commission or Public Service Commission. States regulate the services that utilities offer, determine the rates they can charge for these services, regulate reliability and safety standards, and set standards for financial practices of the utilities. Virtually all states still utilize the traditional rate case methodology for most IOU and UDC services, although they have begun experimenting with incentive ratemaking in some cases. It is important to note that no two state agencies regulate exactly alike. So with 50 states, we also have 50 different ways of doing business.

FERC is responsible for regulating all wholesale transactions, transmission services, and ISOs (except in Texas). Most wholesale transactions are regulated under market-based rates although entities that hold large market shares are required to use cost-of-service-based pricing. Transmission services and ISOs are regulated under a traditional cost-of-service-based methodology.

With the growth of distributed energy resources (DERs) regulators must develop new rates to determine how much the utility company should pay owners of DERs when they provide services to the grid. Services include selling energy (kWh) back onto the grid as well as providing capacity, ancillary services, controllable loads to reduce peak demand, and the ability to defer transmission or distribution upgrades. Regulators must also determine whether customers with DERs should be served under standard rates schedules for the services they buy from the grid, or whether special charges should apply. Traditional rates were not designed with the concept that customers might be prosumers — entities that sometimes buy services from the grid and at other times sell services to the grid.

The first wave of DERs selling energy to the grid comprised cogeneration and renewable units selling power under the rules of PURPA. PURPA mandated that utilities should pay the avoided cost, meaning whatever it would have cost the utility to generate the power using their own units. Once PURPA outlined this concept, it was up to the state regulators to determine the avoided cost for each utility. Later, the concept of avoided cost was amended to be the market price in competitive ISO-facilitated wholesale markets.

The next wave of DERs comprised rooftop solar installations. These resources did not fall under PURPA pricing, and pricing was set in each state by the state regulators. In many states, the concept of net metering was used. Under net metering, utilities simply measure the amount of energy used by a customer, subtract the amount of energy the customer put onto the grid, and then calculate a bill based on the difference. In essence, net metering pays owners of DERs the retail rate for the energy put onto the grid. As the number of rooftop solar systems grows, utilities and regulators have become concerned about the impacts of net metering. It is not clear whether this methodology truly reflects the value of the energy put onto the grid and whether customers with rooftop solar are paying the true cost of their interconnection to the grid. For instance, on a cloudy day a solar customer requires full capacity from the utility to serve their loads, yet since a significant amount of a utility's capacity costs are collected in the variable portion of the rate, a customer that has reduced its bill significantly through net metering may not be paying its fair share of fixed capacity costs. Or alternately, solar customers may be located at a spot where they are providing significant benefits to the grid for which they are not being compensated.

As of 2019, numerous state commissions are holding proceedings to determine the value DERs provide to the grid as well as the costs, and then to determine how to properly reflect these in charges and payments. Alternatives include restructured rate designs for all customers, unique rate classes with rate designs specific for customers with DERs, alternative methodologies for paying for services the DERs provide, payments based on the time of day services are provided, or some combination of these. Since different parties have different goals, proceedings to determine how rates are set are proving to be contentious, and it appears it may take some time for any consensus on new paradigms.

The Future of Regulation

As we will see in the next section, regulation of the electric industry has changed significantly over recent years and is still in flux. Because regulatory authority is shared between federal and state agencies, the U.S. electric industry is subject to a wide variety of regulatory methods and market structures. It is likely that electric regulation will continue to evolve well into the future.

What you will learn:

- What restructuring is

- The arguments for why restructuring of the electric industry can provide benefits to consumers

- How markets mature as they are restructured

- The necessary components for a competitive marketplace

- How these components are implemented

11

SECTION ELEVEN: THE CONCEPTS OF MARKET RESTRUCTURING

The term deregulation is heard commonly in discussions about the electricity market. This, of course, is a misnomer. There is no such thing as deregulation in a market where key sectors are and will remain dominated by regulated monopolies. Even in sectors such as generation and retail sales, where competition can work effectively, the nature of electricity will result in all market participants competing in an environment of ongoing regulatory involvement. Consider, for instance, that a system operator must keep supply and demand in balance at all times, that one market participant's actions potentially impact everyone on the grid, and that disturbances travel quickly throughout regions. And then consider the value our society places on electric service. You can easily see why regulation must play a role in all sectors of the business to ensure safe and reliable service. So again, deregulation is not really what we are experiencing in the electric industry — what we have is market restructuring. And by market restructuring, we mean changes in regulatory rules that alter control, ownership, or regulatory mechanisms of specific industry sectors resulting in increased competition.

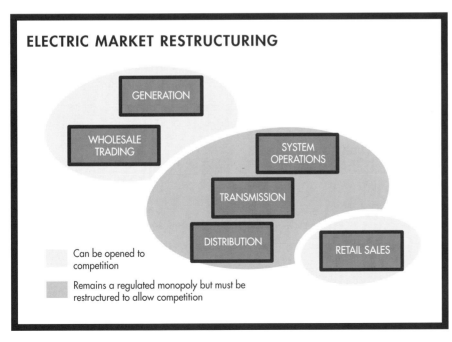

ELECTRIC MARKET RESTRUCTURING

GENERATION

WHOLESALE TRADING

SYSTEM OPERATIONS

TRANSMISSION

DISTRIBUTION

RETAIL SALES

Can be opened to competition

Remains a regulated monopoly but must be restructured to allow competition

Due to the integrated nature of the traditional electric business, we must consider restructuring of all market sectors if we are to introduce competition into any of them. Failure to do so would create a facade of competition without truly creating an environment that can allow it to work. The sectors where we can introduce competition are generation, wholesale trading, and retail sales. Transmission, system operations, and distribution services are clearly monopoly functions, at least for the foreseeable future, but must be modified to allow for competition in other sectors.

We discussed what the different market structures might look like after restructuring in Section Nine. In this section we will discuss the concepts that support creating a new market structure and the implementation steps necessary to get there. These concepts are especially important to understand now because much of the U.S. is in flux relative to market restructuring. Many years into the restructuring process, the country is still stuck with no uniform vision. Some states and regions have moved far down the road to competition, others not at all. And unfortunately there is no clear federal policy for moving to unified markets. Thus, we can assume that anyone involved in the industry will be enmeshed in market restructuring uncertainties for quite some time.

Why Restructuring?

As you will soon learn, restructuring is a messy business. It costs a lot of money, market participants are forced to learn new ways of doing business, regulators lose control over market activities, and in some cases outcomes do not always benefit customers. So why bother?

The goal of a market structure should be to benefit customers by fostering reliable service, reasonable prices, fairly predictable bills, and to encourage innovation in the services provided. Many would argue that the first century of vertically integrated utilities did an effective job of meeting those criteria, at least until issues with nuclear generation and rising oil prices arose. Beginning in the 1970s, a number of utilities were forced to raise rates due to cost overruns on nuclear construction (largely due to changing safety regulations during the construction process) and the rise in fuel costs. Coupled with a general philosophical trend toward deregulation of U.S. industries (including airlines, natural gas, and telecom) this led to a reconsideration of the benefits and necessity of vertical monopoly utilities. As the value of restructuring was (and continues to be) considered, a number of important questions arose:

- Can a competitive generation sector provide lower prices than regulated utility generation?

- Can competitive generation and wholesale marketing sectors result in adequate or improved reliability of supply?

- Will efficiencies resulting from a competitive wholesale trading marketplace result in lower prices?

- Will innovation in competitive retail services provide customer benefits that outweigh any negative aspects of competition?

Various market observers would answer these questions differently, and given the immaturity of electric deregulation, no one yet has the answers. Many would say that deregulation has worked well in U.S. natural gas markets, where prices have fallen dramatically when supply is robust but risen just as dramatically when supply is tight. Meanwhile reliability has been enhanced and new services have offered market participants more choices. Some would contend that electric competition is now providing similar benefits in some regions of the U.S.

The European Union, which in 1999 committed itself to competitive generation and retail sales markets across all of its member countries, lists its reasons for restructuring as follows[1]:

- To increase efficiency by introducing competitive forces into the electricity market.

- To eliminate distortions in competitive conditions that cause enormous price differentials among member states.

- To lower prices relative to the U.S. and Australia.

- To improve essential public services to all customers.

- To reduce needs for expensive reserve capacity by integrating markets.

- To reduce resource waste that results in pollution.

- To give customers the right to choose services that match their needs.

- To improve customer service provided by electricity companies.

Whether these benefits will be achieved is an open question, but few can argue the validity of these reasons for restructuring electric markets. In the end, it simply comes down to the question of what creates more benefits for consumers — a marketplace driven by competition or one controlled by regulation?

---

[1]Summarized from *Opening Up to Choice*, available at:
http://europa.eu.int/comm/energy/electricity/publications/doc/electricity_brochure_en.pdf

Market Evolution under Deregulation

Market restructuring is not an overnight process. It takes a long time to implement, there are lots of bumps in the road, and benefits may not appear for as long as a decade. Consider what has happened in the airline and telecom industries over the last 30 years. While the process has taken decades to evolve (and is still evolving) for these industries, does anyone doubt the benefits to consumers? For anyone old enough to remember the days of the vertical AT&T phone monopoly, simply consider the multitude of services available today compared to the plain black dial phones of the past.

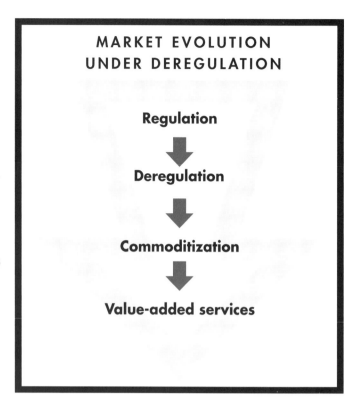

MARKET EVOLUTION UNDER DEREGULATION

Regulation

Deregulation

Commoditization

Value-added services

To put the process of market evolution under deregulation in perspective, let's consider four phases of market evolution — regulation, deregulation, commoditization, and value-added services — as they provide an excellent framework from which to review the changes that may occur with restructuring in a specific region (remembering that different sectors will be at different phases in different states and regions in the U.S.). While the generation, wholesale trading, and retail sales sectors will likely mature through these phases, they may not do so simultaneously but rather will do so at different times in different regions. And in some regions they may even remain regulated or may go back to regulated after initially being deregulated. In almost all cases the transmission, system operations, and distribution sectors will remain in the regulation phase, though regulation will have to be restructured to recognize the changes in the competitive sectors.

Regulation

This phase is characterized by the dominance of regulation and lack of competition across the delivery chain. Transactions are generally highly structured and usually long-term in nature. Prices are fixed, buyers and sellers are relatively few, barriers to market entry are significant, vertically integrated utilities dominate the marketplace, and customer choices are minimal. Prices are cost-of-service-based with little or no

11

flexibility, and decisions to invest in infrastructure or innovation are highly influenced by support (or lack thereof) of regulators.

Prior to 1992, all of the U.S. electricity industry was in the regulation phase. Utilities or closely aligned generation agencies owned all generation, transmission, and distribution and operated their systems as a unified whole. Customers had little choice but to buy electric supply from their local utility.

Deregulation

In the deregulation phase, rules are loosened in some sectors and barriers to entry are broken down to allow competition to come into the market. As the number of competitors increases, transactions become more flexible and customers attempt to benefit from increasing choice and competition. Regulation still controls much of the way business is transacted, but it is designed to encourage a level playing field among competi-

---

EXAMPLES OF ELECTRIC SERVICES IN THE MARKET PHASES

Regulation

- Utility distribution services

- Transmission services

- System operations in states without ISOs

- All sectors in states where full vertical integration remains in effect

Deregulation

- Electric supply to customers in states where the utility sells regulated commodity in competition with marketing companies

- Power purchases by utilities from merchant power generators

- System operations in states with ISOs

Commoditization

- Electric supply to industrial customers in states with robust customer choice programs

- Wholesale electricity trading in ISO markets and other regions where liquid trading exists

Value-added Services

- ESCO services to industrial and commercial customers

- Financial services

- Combined commodity services (electric, gas, telecom, etc.) sold by a retail marketer

- Distributed energy resources

---

tors and to foster competition in sectors that have been opened. Services in the competitive sectors (which may include generation, wholesale trading, and retail sales) become more diverse and may be tailored to individual customers. While system operations remains highly regulated, prices for services such as reserves and transmission

able to cause these situations to occur by purposely removing generation from the market (by taking it down for maintenance during a critical hour). Thus it is necessary to encourage new generation construction in the marketplace, to encourage adequate transmission to let geographically remote suppliers compete, to find mechanisms that encourage utilities to divest of rate base generation, and to carefully review any regulatory protections that would favor existing generation units. In the absence of a fully competitive supply market, regulators must revert to regulatory solutions that include price caps, bidding restrictions, generation availability requirements, and/or profit controls. It should be noted that sufficient generation capacity is an additional requirement for a competitive market. There may be any number of generators supplying a given market, but without sufficient capacity the market is beholden to them in the same way it is if there is no competition. Some regions have implemented mandatory capacity markets to ensure sufficient generation resources.

Fair Access to Transmission

The need for many suppliers goes hand in hand with the need for fair access to transmission. If a supplier cannot get access to transmission, it cannot get its supply to market. Some markets in the U.S. have benefited less from new merchant generation than expected because transmission issues have prevented these units from fully functioning in the marketplace.

Establishing fair access to transmission is one reason for creating an Independent System Operator that, in addition to other responsibilities, is responsible for allocating transmission access. The ISO is not controlled by any market participant (unlike the wheeling model, where transmission access is controlled by the incumbent utility). Rules must be developed that give every market participant the same opportunity to use transmission and to allocate transmission access based on fair criteria — usually who is willing to pay the most. Any existing firm transmission rights contracts would ideally be bought out, otherwise certain market participants have favored access to the system. And in some cases where constraints in the existing transmission system impede open trading, market rules must foster new transmission construction. Rules must also be developed that determine how the new transmission is paid for so that costs are allocated fairly to the market participants who benefit from it.

Unbiased System Operations

In addition to allocating transmission, the system operator must operate the system to ensure reliability and balance supply and demand in real time. This can work only if the system operator is in control of the generation assets serving the system. As loads grow, units must be ramped up. As loads fall, units must be ramped down. And sometimes, units must be redispatched from desired schedules due to locational issues. In a competitive market, generation owners are understandably reluctant to turn dispatch control of their units over to another entity unless they are convinced that the entity is running those units in an unbiased manner. Thus the requirement for a truly independent ISO.

Demand-side Competition

To ensure market liquidity, in addition to many sellers there must also be many buyers. One without the other does not make for a fully competitive market. Sellers cannot be tied to selling to a single utility procurement group — doing so simply creates a buyers' monopoly that must be regulated. To have a competitive market there must be the opportunity for end-use customers to choose to buy directly from suppliers rather than through their utility. Clearly the way to create the largest number of buyers is to completely remove the utility from offering supply services. This has been done and can work. But many states are reluctant to open markets simultaneously to all customers, and experience certainly has shown that there can be advantages to phasing in customer choice. Many argue that a sufficient number of buyers can be created by allowing only large commercial and industrial customers the choice of supply. Since they make up significant demand in terms of load (even if not in terms of number of accounts) this is often enough to create market liquidity. Another way to increase buyers is to also allow aggregated groups of smaller customers to buy directly. Some states are providing this opportunity through programs like municipal aggregation where cities buy power on behalf of groups of customers.

A second key requirement on the demand side is to create markets where buyers become responsive to short-term electricity prices. By this we mean a market in which high wholesale prices will encourage buyers to curtail their usage until prices fall. Many current market structures do not provide for this as end users often pay average utility prices that are fixed for at least a year at a time. If wholesale prices spike to the equivalent of $5/kWh, end users in a traditional market have little incentive to care — they will likely continue to run their air conditioners at full tilt because they are paying the utility average price of $.10/kWh. This perhaps is one of the biggest factors in arguing for electric restructuring. As long as customers don't get price signals (and therefore do not have the opportunity to refuse the use of high-priced power), there is nothing to restrain market power and bad business decisions by utility executives and/or regulators except after-the-fact corrections by regulators. The key to facilitating demand response to price is to create an infrastructure that gives customers the appropriate tools. This requires meters with hourly data that can be accessed by customers in real time, some means of communicating hourly prices to customers, and an ISO market structure that allows loads to bid into markets in the same way that generation participates.

Distribution without Impediments to Competition

Also critical for a functioning competitive market are distribution services that foster, not impede, customer choice. There are a number of service issues that are critical:

- Providing access to meter data for both customers and marketers.

- Providing default suppliers for customers that don't choose or can't find a marketer.

- Determining whether the utility will be allowed to offer supply services, and, if so, setting an equitable price.

- Determining how societal programs such as demand side management and environmental programs will be paid for.

- Setting rules for customers that choose to self-generate, including stand-by rates, interconnection charges, and the opportunity to sell excess power and other services back to the grid.

- Determining how transition costs associated with restructuring will be allocated.

- Determining how costs are allocated between distribution and supply services.

Many a budding competitive market has been stymied by just two of these factors — how the default rate is set for utility supply services (if it's too low, no marketer can compete) and how meter data is made available to marketers (without meter data, marketers can't bill their customers).

Opportunities for Hedging Risks

Prices in competitive markets — especially for a commodity like electricity — are volatile. Electricity prices fluctuate rapidly based on supply and demand. Demands at 6 p.m. are often double what they are at 6 a.m. This means twice as much generation is required — at much higher prices. And as gas prices fluctuate, availability of hydro power comes and goes, hot or cold weather drives demand, and large units go down for maintenance, price fluctuations from $20/MWh to $250/MWh are not unexpected. Many market participants cannot handle such fluctuations. Thus regulators must always be cognizant of creating stable rules and market structures that can help foster the development of financial markets for risk hedging.

Creating a Competitive Market

Now that you understand the requirements for a competitive electric marketplace, let's take a look at the issues involved in its actual implementation. As we have seen repeatedly in the U.S., the move from a regulated monopoly market structure to a competitive one is no simple task. Regulators and legislators have a number of key issues they must address if the transition is to be successful. These include how to create a competitive generation sector, how to ensure adequate transmission capacity, how to create a functioning ISO with viable trading arrangements, how to transition to customer choice, how to regulate the remaining transmission and distribution assets, and how to ensure reliability.

Transitioning Generation

As long as generation remains part of a vertical utility and is subject to rate base treatment, there cannot be a fully competitive supply sector because these assets will benefit from cross subsidies not available to merchant generators. Options for opening up the generation sector include ordering the utilities to separate generation functions into a subsidiary company (and regulating activities between the newly created subsidiaries with market affiliate rules), encouraging the utilities to sell off generation assets (known as divestiture), requiring utilities to give up control of generation by auctioning off rights to blocks of generation capacity, or setting specific limits on the market share any one generation entity is allowed to own and control. Forced divestiture (i.e., without a utility's agreement) is legally problematic since it could be considered a "taking" under the U.S. Constitution.

An additional generation transition issue is how to deal with generation assets that may not be well-suited to a competitive environment. Examples include nuclear generation (due to its inability to ramp up and down and the need to cover capital costs that may have been allocated to customers over a long number of years), QFs (due to laws that require utilities to take QF output), certain types of renewable generation (because they are potentially more expensive to build but less harmful to the environment and may operate intermittently), and supply provided by DERs. Often regulators must create a category for nuclear generation and QFs that is called regulatory "must take." This requires the system operator to take the output regardless of price. Mechanisms must also be established for generators that must run due to locational transmission issues that prevent power from being brought into a demand zone. These facilities are called "must run." Regulators must then come up with a mechanism to allocate costs of must-take and must-run generation to consumers. Regulators or legislators may also wish to encourage development of renewable generation for the societal benefit of a cleaner environment. A common solution is a renewable portfolio requirement. A portfolio requirement sets a percentage of generation that each market participant must obtain from renewable energy. An alternative is to offer tax credits or other economic incentives for building renewable generation. And as discussed in Sections Nine and Ten, regulators must create rules that foster market participation by DERs.

Creating a Robust Transmission Market

As we have seen earlier in this book, creating supply choice does little to open a competitive market without also ensuring adequate transmission access so that suppliers can easily compete in all areas of the market without being stymied by transmission congestion. Given current and pervasive opposition to the construction of transmission in the U.S., this is a significant issue. It appears that the best solution may be the creation of transmission-only companies that are regulated under traditional rate-of-return methods. These companies can significantly expand earnings only by expanding rate base (i.e., by building new transmission), which should strongly incent them to work with local communities to come to acceptable solutions for the construction of new transmission. Also important is moving from local transmission planning based on reliability needs to a broader regional planning process that also considers market benefits.

A related issue is how to handle existing long-term transmission agreements. Such agreements, if they control a significant amount of transmission capacity, will prevent a competitive market from evolving.

Finally, in areas where transmission congestion is prevalent, market participants must often pay transmission congestion charges that are in excess of the standard transmission costs. Since this creates a significant cost uncertainty, it is important to create mechanisms that market participants can use to lay off this risk. This is done by creating a mechanism called FTRs, or financial transmission rights. FTRs are auctioned periodically and allow buyers to lock in congestion costs associated with a specific transmission path. There is also a need for long-term management of congestion price risk to allow new generation projects to develop without excessive uncertainty. Thus ISOs are beginning to consider creating long-term financial transmission rights.

Creating an ISO

There is no way around it — there must be an independent unbiased system operator for a competitive market to function. Creating an ISO requires cooperation between the states and FERC, since ISOs are FERC-jurisdictional (except in Texas) yet the utilities that will give up the system operations function are state-jurisdictional. And if utilities are not willing to voluntarily turn control of their systems to the ISO, regulators must be willing to order them to do so. As we have discussed elsewhere, the structure of the ISO's trading arrangements are critically important. If the rules are flawed, market consequences can be severe. Fortunately, we now have some good operating experience from various ISOs in the U.S. and around the world, and our knowledge of what works and what doesn't is expanding rapidly.

Transitioning to Customer Choice

Transitioning to customer choice is perhaps even more critical than all the other issues we've discussed. The efforts to create competition are a moot point if customers choose not to participate. Critical issues include customer education, avoiding the temptation to give customers the option to stay with the utility at fixed prices that do not reflect market fluctuations, and letting the market develop sufficiently before dumping customers into the fray. Many observers now believe that it makes most sense to first allow large customers to choose, then transition in customer choice to smaller customers as markets mature.

Continued Regulation of Transmission and Distribution

Regulators must continue to regulate the monopoly functions of transmission and distribution. Options range from traditional cost-of-service to various forms of performance-based ratemaking. It is critically important to vigilantly monitor any set of rules for signs that it may create barriers to competition.

Ensuring Reliability

One of the hottest issues in today's environment is how to ensure reliability in a competitive marketplace. Reliability breaks down into multiple issues — ensuring adequate supply capacity on a long-term and short-term basis in regions with significant renewable generation, ensuring adequate system flexibility, ensuring adequate reserves, ensuring adequate transmission, and ensuring sufficient investment in distribution construction and maintenance. The latter issue can be handled by regulation of the distribution monopoly just as it is under traditional markets. Ensuring adequate supply flexibility and reserves in the short term is an issue of trading arrangement design. Ensuring long-term supply and transmission is a more thorny issue. The general concept is that as supply drops, prices will rise. Higher prices encourage new generation or transmission, which enhances supply, causing prices to drop back down. And if you believe in competitive markets, it all works out. Unfortunately, there are often numerous barriers to new generation — NIMBY activists who block construction, uncertain returns given volatile electric prices, and lack of capital for speculative construction. And if generation takes five years to build, what happens to customers in the meantime?

A number of options have been discussed and, in some cases, implemented. Initially many markets attempted to simply let the market work it out. To do so, however, requires mechanisms that allow customers to respond to price. If prices get too high and the market structure permits customers to respond, they will likely use power in different ways or sign long-term contracts with generators to guarantee prices. However, concerns about rising prices and/or falling reliability have generally led policymakers to conclude that the unique nature of electricity may not be well-suited to total dependence on markets. Many regions now give ISOs or state agencies the power to forecast future generating capacity needed to ensure reliability multiple years into the future. The ISOs or state agencies then allocate a capacity responsibility to each Load Serving Entity (LSE) based on that entity's market share. The LSE is then obligated to make sufficient long-term supply arrangements to cover its allocated responsibility or be placed into a mandatory auction to acquire the needed capacity. An alternative to such an auction is to penalize entities that fail to provide sufficient capacity. Either way, the capacity obligation provides a long-term guaranteed revenue stream for generators, hopefully resulting in construction of sufficient capacity.

Settlements

As you might imagine the shift to numerous market participants and multiple energy, reserves, and capacity markets creates the need for additional accounting and tracking of transactions to ensure money flows to those providing necessary services. This important function is provided by a centralized entity that tracks thousands of power transactions and determines who is owed (and by whom) for each. For wholesale transactions this is typically handled by the ISO.

Future Distribution Restructuring

To date, restructuring of electric markets has generally focused on wholesale markets and, in some cases, retail supply. As penetrations of DERs grow, regulators are forced to consider whether the distribution function should be restructured as well.

During wholesale restructuring, concerns over market power of utilities led to formation of ISOs to ensure fair access to transmission and to facilitate non-biased wholesale markets. Some in the industry now believe that a similar concept will be required to allow owners and operators of DERs fair access into local and wholesale electric markets. Concepts include changing the role of the distribution utility into a Distributed Services Platform Provider (DSPP), creating an unbiased third-party Distribution System Operator (DSO), or use of blockchains for peer-to-peer trading. The DSPP model is being implemented in New York state and will task distribution utilities will fulfilling three roles:

- Distribution grid operator that is capable of integrating high penetrations of DERs.

- Distribution market manager that manages power flows associated with DERs in real time and is responsible for creating opportunities for DER owners to monetize the provision of products and services to the distribution grid or to other local market participants.

- Intermediary between retail consumers and the wholesale marketplace so that DER services may be sold into wholesale markets.

An alternative is to simply create an independent DSO that would serve the same role on distribution systems as the ISO serves on the transmission system and leave other functions to non-regulated market participants. Some in the industry have even suggested doing away with central control of distribution-level markets and instead using blockchain technology to allow all market participants to directly trade with each other. Any of these concepts will result in significant restructuring at the distribution level and open the door for new services and new market participants. As of 2019, it appears that the next wave of restructuring will likely focus on the distribution system.

What you will learn:

- The recent history of electric market restructuring in the U.S.

- The current status of restructuring in the U.S.

- What different states have done and are doing

- What has been done elsewhere in the world

- Key issues that have arisen during the restructuring process

12

12

SECTION TWELVE: THE HISTORY OF ELECTRIC MARKET RESTRUCTURING

The door to electric market restructuring cracked open in the United States in 1978 when a change in federal law allowed private owners of cogeneration units to sell power into utility grids. Prior to this time, the U.S. had no non-utility-owned generation (other than generation owned by groups of utilities in power agencies or generation owned by federal power agencies). But it wasn't until the 1990s that we began to see the actual implications of restructured markets. This is when issues such as merchant generation, transmission access, ISOs, and customer choice programs came to the forefront. Due to a shared regulatory jurisdiction, market restructuring requires cooperation from both federal and state regulators. This has worked well in some cases and not so well in others. Because of the states' role in regulating utilities, the status of market restructuring varies widely across the U.S. Some states have gone well down the path to competition, while others have held on to traditional regulation. In this section we will look first at the history of federal government deregulation, then move on to a discussion of the states.

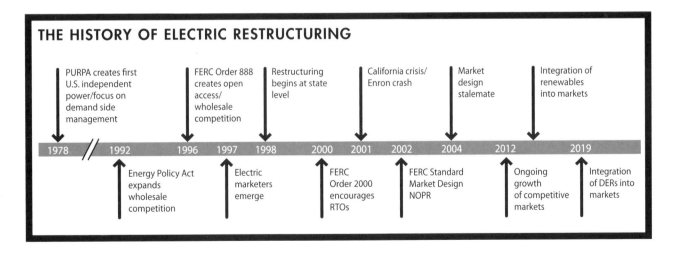

THE HISTORY OF ELECTRIC RESTRUCTURING

PURPA creates first U.S. independent power/focus on demand side management — 1978

Energy Policy Act expands wholesale competition — 1992

FERC Order 888 creates open access/wholesale competition — 1996

Electric marketers emerge — 1997

Restructuring begins at state level — 1998

FERC Order 2000 encourages RTOs — 2000

California crisis/Enron crash — 2001

FERC Standard Market Design NOPR — 2002

Market design stalemate — 2004

Ongoing growth of competitive markets — 2012

Integration of renewables into markets — 2019

Integration of DERs into markets — 2019

Furthering Open Access Transmission — FERC Order 888

Seeing the problems the existing policies were creating, and mindful of the success of open-access policies in the natural gas industry, FERC opened a proceeding to look into the issues of transmission access, transmission pricing, and stranded costs. This resulted in FERC Order 888, issued in April 1996. Order 888:

- Required that all transmission owners subject to FERC jurisdiction provide whole-sale transmission services to all parties under the same terms and conditions that they provide service to their own generation, with the exception that utilities were able to reserve transmission for service to their own native loads (meaning end users of the utility).

- Required utilities to functionally separate generation, transmission, power control, and distribution activities.

- Identified six ancillary services that utilities must provide in adjunct with transmission service and allowed utilities to develop rates for these services.

- Found that if stranded costs are caused by departing wholesale customers, the utility could recoup these costs from the departing customers, providing the utility first tried to mitigate them (e.g., finding new customers to replace the costs).

- Encouraged, but did not require, utilities to create Independent System Operators (ISOs) and laid out criteria for FERC approval of them.

ORDER 888 PRINCIPLES FOR APPROVAL OF ISOs

The ISO:

1. Must have a fair and non-discriminatory governance structure.

2. May not have financial interests in any market participants.

3. Must have a single, open-access tariff for the entire area served by the ISO.

4. Is responsible for system security.

5. May control system dispatch for pool or bilateral arrangements.

6. Can manage transmission constraints.

7. Has incentives for efficiency.

8. Has pricing mechanisms for transmission and ancillary services that promote market efficiency.

9. Must post transmission availability in real time on electronic bulletin boards.

10. Must coordinate with adjacent control areas.

11. Must have a dispute resolution process.

Order 888 put in place a number of key conventions that still drive the way the electricity industry operates today. The order required open-access transmission tariffs (often called OAT tariffs) whereby utilities must treat other parties' transactions in the same manner they treat power transactions performed internally. It required the utilities to functionally create separation among their generation, transmission, power control, and distribution departments (although FERC did not have the authority to order the actual breakup of the vertical utility). It intro-

> ## STRANDED COSTS
>
> One of the most contentious issues regulators must consider during restructuring is how to handle stranded costs. Stranded costs are utility costs associated with assets acquired under prior regulatory rules that are in excess of the market value of these assets once the market is restructured. An example is a high-priced power plant that will no longer be run once lower-cost merchant power comes into a restructured marketplace. Utility shareholders will argue that the above-market costs should be paid by consumers since the unit was initially built under the assumption that the utility was responsible for serving all loads in its territory. Companies attempting to compete with utilities will argue that providing full cost coverage for stranded assets makes it impossible for competitors to compete effectively and thus deprives consumers of the benefits of competition. A key job for regulators is to accurately identify stranded costs and then collect them in a manner that is fair to utility shareholders, but does not impede the development of a competitive market.

duced the concept of ancillary services as separate and distinct and allowed utilities to charge for providing them. And, much to the relief of the utilities, it embraced the concept that stranded costs should be recoverable. Although this applied only to wholesale issues, it gave utilities a good precedent to quote when the discussion came up later in state restructuring proceedings. Order 888 also encouraged, though it did not require, the formation of ISOs to create "organized wholesale markets" and laid out 11 principles required for approval of ISO tariffs (see box on page 160).

Wholesale trading grew quickly after Order 888 was issued — from approximately 100 million kWh in 1996 to close to 4.5 billion kWh in 2000[2]. However, until states began restructuring, the only buyers were still the utilities. Restructuring in some key states including California, New York, and Pennsylvania began in the late 1990s, opening the door for marketers and generators to sell directly to end-use customers.

---

[2]It should be noted, however, that later events revealed that some of these transactions were sham transactions used by marketers to boost apparent revenues.

underestimated either the strength of opposition to SMD or its ability to push things forward in the face of opposition. After legislators from southern and northwestern states threatened to hold up FERC's budget authorizations and then proposed bills that would explicitly limit FERC's authority to impose SMD, FERC backed down.

In 2003, FERC issued a new white paper that indicated a reduced emphasis on uniformity with greater tolerance for regional variations. It also suggested that transition periods could be as long as 10 years. FERC's attempts to create a uniform market structure across the U.S., or even to foster a rapid transition to regional uniform markets, appeared at least temporarily stymied. This left us with a fragmented market characterized by seven functioning ISOs/RTOs and other regions with no ISO/RTO plans.

Ongoing Growth of ISO Markets

As of 2019, the divide between organized competitive wholesale markets run by an ISO and regions sticking with no organized markets remains. However, recent years have seen the growth in ISO markets as numerous utilities have made the voluntary decision to join ISOs and have received regulatory approvals to do so. Many utilities have concluded that participation in an ISO provides benefits such as reduced reserves costs, improved grid reliability, more optimal use of transmission, lower costs of integrating renewable power, and access to larger markets for sales of excess power. PJM began life as an ISO with approximately 56,000 MW of generation in its market area and has since expanded to over 180,000 MW. PJM has grown through integration of utilities such as AEP, Allegheny Energy, Dayton Power and Light, Dominion, Duquesne, and Exelon, which initially did not participate in ISOs. They have also added utilities that have opted to move from MISO to PJM such as First Energy and Duke Energy Ohio. MISO too has added new members including Ameren, MidAmerican, and Entergy's Arkansas, Louisiana, Mississippi, and Texas utilities. In 2015 SPP expanded to add utilities in parts of six additional states. And, as discussed in Section Eight, a number of utilities in neighboring states now participate in California ISO real-time markets through the Energy Imbalance Market. As of 2019, over 63% of the generation capacity in the U.S. is in ISO markets. In addition, discussions concerning expanding CAISO or SPP further into neighboring states and/or creating a new western ISO are ongoing.

State Restructuring

While it is FERC's role to get wholesale trading, transmission, and system operation markets working, it is the role of the states to consider retail competition and breakup of the vertical utilities. Some states have chosen to do nothing, while others have moved aggressively into restructuring the role and business structure of the utilities. In many cases it was the high-price states that took the lead, given pressure from industrial customers who desire access to lower-cost sources of electricity. The first state to implement retail access was Rhode Island in 1997. By 2006, 20 states plus the District of Columbia had implemented some form of retail competition.

Key issues for the states include:

- Which market structure to adopt.

- Which trading arrangements to adopt.

- Whether to support movement to an ISO or RTO.

- How to foster the separation of the vertical utility functions.

- Whether to allow retail access, and if so, how.

- How to continue regulation of the continuing monopoly utility function.

In general, states that have chosen to restructure have done it in one of three ways — transitioning existing power pools into ISO structures (New England states, New York, PJM states), creating new statewide or regional ISOs (California, Texas, and portions of the Midwest), or implementing restructuring without putting in place new competitive wholesale market structures (the rest).

We discussed market structures and trading arrangements in Section Nine, as well as ISOs and RTOs earlier in this section. Following is a discussion of the remaining key issues faced by states and how they've been handled to date. Suffice it to say that no two states have implemented restructuring exactly alike, and each state is a unique case.

Separating the Vertical Utility Functions

As we have discussed, it is necessary to separate the utility functions of generation, transmission, system operations, and distribution to provide opportunities for competition. Absent some breakup of utility functions, non-utility competitors will always be looking in from the outside and will not be able to compete on a level playing field. Actions states have taken range from simply requiring utilities to create new separate departments (with affiliate rules to define behavior between departments) to strongly encouraging utilities to divest of generation and in some cases transmission assets. Another option is to have utilities move their generation assets to separate subsidiary companies.

Allowing Retail Access

In general, the decision for retail access comes down to allowing all customers to choose, allowing none to choose, or defining specific classes of customers that are eligible to choose. A popular solution is to allow only large commercial and industrial customers to choose. Another is to allow all customers to choose competitive supply but also to continue a regulated default supply service from the utility, often with capped rates. Some states have skirted the issue by allowing customers to leave utility supply on a case-by-case basis that requires specific commission approval or by experimenting with virtual access. Virtual access offers customers the option of having the utility buy power at market rates for the customer rather than receiving a traditional average utility supply cost. An additional form of choice implemented in some states is Community Choice Aggregation (CCA). CCA allows local governmental entities or special districts to provide supply services to customers within their jurisdictional area. Meanwhile the utility remains responsible for delivery as with other retail choice methods. As of 2019, eight U.S. states have enacted legislation providing for CCA.

12

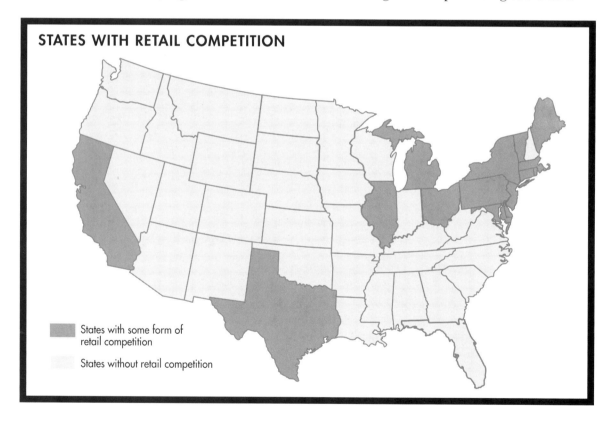

STATES WITH RETAIL COMPETITION

States with some form of retail competition

States without retail competition

Continued Regulation of the Monopoly Function

The mechanism for continued regulation of the monopoly function is often one of the most contentious issues and can determine everything about the attractiveness and success of retail access options. The issues to be considered are discussed in Section Eleven, but it is worth reiterating that the devil is in the details, and seemingly minor decisions such as how meter data will be transmitted among market participants can have huge impacts. Many states that have implemented retail choice continue to work on such details, and it is important to remember that restructuring is an ongoing effort, not a one-time event.

Current Status of Retail Choice in the U.S.

As of 2019, 15 states plus the District of Columbia have established retail choice for some or all consumers. These jurisdictions represent about 43% of the power sold in the U.S. although in some states only a portion of the power sold is under competitive retail choice (with the remainder sold by utilities under regulated default programs). As of the end of 2017, about 21% of U.S. loads purchased their supply from competitive retail providers. This has grown significantly over the last decade and appears likely to continue to grow.

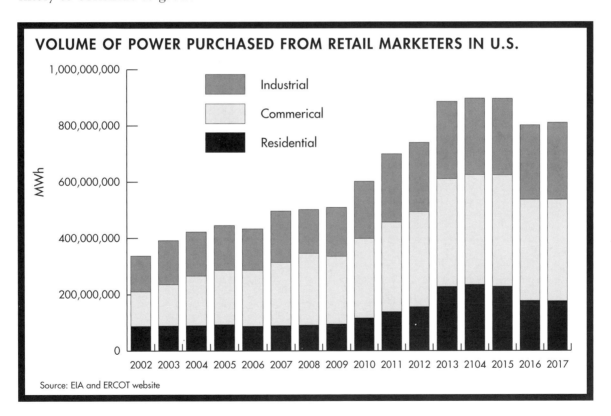

VOLUME OF POWER PURCHASED FROM RETAIL MARKETERS IN U.S.

Source: EIA and ERCOT website

California — A Bad Retail Competition Experience

It is unlikely that any reader of this book on the electric industry has not been exposed to some coverage of the California energy crisis of 2000–2001. And most have probably heard as much as they care to on the subject. If you are well versed in California's experience in electric restructuring, you are encouraged to skip the following discussion. If, on the other hand, you do not fully understand what occurred in California, read on for a great lesson in politics and market dynamics.

California implemented electric deregulation on April 1, 1998. In the first years (1998–1999) wholesale electric prices dropped — so much so that some market participants in the Pacific Northwest accused California of creating a market structure that would purposely drive prices down to the benefit of Californians and the detriment of surrounding states that export large volumes to California. Retail access markets were active and things seemed to be going well.

Suddenly everything changed. In the summer of 2000 high market prices began occurring in peak hours, and by fall prices were high in almost all hours. Wholesale power costs rose from $7 billion in 1999 to $27 billion in 2000. The utilities[4] were unable to pass these costs through to their customers due to the structure of the market. Thus they were put in the position of buying power at an average wholesale price of $317/MWh in December 2000 while reselling it to their customers at rates in the $45/MWh range. The utilities had nowhere to turn to make up the revenue shortfall and soon could no longer pay the generators for power. Power was already short due to a low hydro year and numerous generators offline for maintenance. (It now appears that some generators may have purposely removed their facilities from the market because they were not getting paid or to drive prices higher.) By January 2001, the California ISO could no longer procure enough generation to serve loads and was left with no alternative but to implement planned rolling blackouts to bring supply and demand in balance.

The State of California was forced to step in as the only creditworthy buyer able to procure supply on behalf of the utilities. The state signed long-term agreements with numerous generators to assure supply at prices and terms that were highly favorable to the generators. Given market conditions at the time, however, the state had little choice but to sign them. These contracts quickly proved to be an embarrassment as spot prices — driven by increased supply and falling demand — fell well below the fixed contract rates, and the state was forced to sell excess power at a loss (although in fairness to the state, it should be noted that the existence of the agreements contributed to stabilization of the market and perhaps helped to drive market prices down). The state found itself with billions of dollars in general fund expenditures for

[4]By utilities we mean Pacific Gas and Electric and Southern California Edison. The situation was different for San Diego Gas and Electric and the municipal utilities.

electricity that was not recovered in electric rates. Pacific Gas and Electric was forced to declare bankruptcy and Southern California Edison nearly did as well.

California suspended retail access to prevent customers from leaving the utilities' supply (to avoid paying for the high-priced state contracts) and went back to the regulated utility model. By 2003, the utilities were back in charge of generating and/or purchasing supply for all customers (except for grandfathered direct-access customers) under a cost-of-service regulation model, and by 2004 the California Public Utilities Commission (CPUC) allowed San Diego Gas and Electric and Southern California Edison to purchase new generating assets within the regulated utility. Meanwhile, California customers who were already paying some of the highest rates in the country were hit with new rate increases to cover the cost of paying off past debts and of covering the high-priced state contracts. The state accused a number of market participants of purposely manipulating the market to raise prices, and information disclosed in subsequent proceedings seemed to indicate that some had indeed done so. FERC ordered a number of refunds and the state came to settlements with other parties.

Meanwhile, Governor Gray Davis was swept out of office in a recall election caused in part by public perception of his failed handling of the crisis and was replaced with former movie star Arnold Schwarzenegger. By early 2006, the three investor-owned utilities were back in the business of providing monopoly service to all but a dwindling group of direct-access customers who were grandfathered from earlier years.

Many who oppose electric restructuring argue that California shows why it is a flawed concept. Others who support restructuring simply believe that it was the California market structure that was flawed — along with a good bit of bad luck. And many who don't support one position or the other are simply scared away from restructuring by the outcome. So why did California's experiment turn out so badly?

California's experience was the result of a series of unfortunate circumstances, many of them self-inflicted. AB 1890, the California bill that set the market structure, was passed unanimously in the state legislature. This perhaps led to much of the problem since the bill included numerous provisions attempting to appeal to everyone. Key factors included:

- A supply dependence on hydro power, which varies significantly from year to year based on weather patterns.
- A low hydro year in 2000 coupled with rising natural gas prices.

- A lack of new generation or transmission built in California for 10 years prior to restructuring.

- An incredibly complex market structure that included bilateral trading for non-utility entities, a requirement that utilities trade through a centralized auction-based exchange that was separate from the ISO, and an ISO that used auction-based markets every hour to acquire ancillary services and to allocate transmission during times of transmission congestion. With day-ahead, hour-ahead, and real-time markets this resulted in over a dozen auctions for energy and capacity for every hour of every day.

- A market design that resulted in the utilities buying all their supply at spot prices. It is estimated that upwards of 80% of California power was being bought at spot market prices whereas in other markets 80% was bought at long-term prices. And the spot prices were determined in auctions where the most expensive unit used during the hour set the market price that was paid to every supplier. So 80% of the state's power was bought at the marginal price.

- A retail market structure that provided end users a fixed rate no matter what happened in the wholesale marketplace. Thus, there was no demand response even as wholesale prices climbed to ridiculous levels. Many analysts believe that the California crisis would never have occurred had end users been exposed to whole-sale prices — many users would have simply reduced energy use at those price levels and the problem would have corrected itself.

- Corporate culture among market participants that seemed to accept the concept that any action that resulted in profits was good, along with a lack of market protections by regulators. Both FERC and the CPUC seemed to enter deregulation believing that the market would take care of any attempts at manipulation. But a complex market structure is rife with opportunities for what traders call "arbitrage," and the California ISO was not given the teeth to police activities that were clearly designed to profit traders in questionable ways.

The California crisis has been studied extensively across the country, and one can only hope regulators and legislators have learned a number of lessons about designing restructured markets. Meanwhile, by the late 2000s California had stabilized its electric markets by returning to a dependence on the three large vertically integrated utilities.

Texas and New York — More Successful Retail Competition Experiences

While the initial retail competition in California did not work out so well, other states have proven that retail competition can work. Texas approved deregulation of the electric industry with Senate Bill 7 passed in 1999. Deregulation began in 2002. All customers of investor-owned utilities (IOUs) in the ERCOT market area then had the choice of remaining with their utility supply or selecting a retail marketer. Customers of munis or co-ops could participate in customer choice only if their utility opted in to deregulation, and by 2012 only one had done so. Originally the incumbent IOUs offered a regulated "price to beat" that allowed customers to avoid choosing a retail marketer. This option was eliminated in 2007 and now all customers in the ERCOT market area purchase competitive supply from retail marketers. While the debate goes on as to whether Texas consumers have benefited from competition, there has been no market blow-up like California, and as of 2019 the Public Utilities Commission of Texas lists about 120 active retail marketers.

New York meanwhile took a different route to deregulation. Deregulation in New York was initiated by the New York Public Services Commission (NYPSC) with release of a policy framework for industry deregulation. With a transitional period that began in 1998, the NYPSC instructed each utility company to begin the process of divesting of electric generation assets. The NYPSC then required each utility to file plans for opening markets to retail competition. Each utility entered into separate agreements with the regulatory agency and various interested market participants resulting in different deregulation plans for each utility. While each utility ultimately provided the choice of retail competition, they also continued to offer default regulated rates. Initial switching to competitive options was mostly by large customers, but over time more and more residential customers have opted to move to competitive options. As of the end of 2018, customers representing 20% of residential loads, 65% of small commercial and industrial (C&I) loads, and 82% of large C&I loads were buying supply from retail marketers.

Restructuring in Other Countries

In these days of increasing globalization, it would be foolish not to look beyond our borders at restructuring efforts in other parts of the world. Concepts and technologies developed elsewhere have the potential to rapidly change the U.S. marketplace. While we won't go into detail on the world electric marketplace, it is important to be aware that electric restructuring is moving rapidly in many places throughout the world and the U.S. is no longer on the forefront of restructuring efforts. The European Union is in the process of bringing retail choice to all customers over the next few years, and full retail customer choice with the equivalent of ISOs has been in effect in New Zealand, the United Kingdom, and parts of Australia for a number of years.

Other countries such as Chile and the Nordic countries of Norway and Sweden have operated competitive generation markets for over a decade. And the Canadian provinces of Alberta and Ontario have implemented competitive markets as well. In 2016, Mexico opened both wholesale and retail markets to competition and Japan opened retail markets to competition prior to implementing wholesale competition. So electric restructuring will continue to be a force worldwide. While the movement toward restructuring has been slow in the U.S. in recent years, it is sure to continue, and those states that have moved well into restructuring will probably never go back to a world of vertical utilities.

12

What you will learn:

- How electric supply and demand fluctuate

- The current supply/demand situation in the U.S.

- How wholesale electricity prices are set

- Why wholesale prices are so volatile

- How the wholesale marketplace works

- How the retail marketplace works

13

SECTION THIRTEEN: MARKET DYNAMICS

Ultimately, all activities in the marketplace are dictated by the end user, who will purchase electricity only so long as it is financially feasible and emotionally rewarding to do so. One of the major sources of inefficiency in the electricity marketplace is the fact that consumers have been shielded from the actual costs of their end-use decisions because most pay an average cost. As described by Sally Hunt, an expert on electricity competition[1], if we ran clothing stores the way we run the electricity market we would offer Armani suits and Gap jeans at the same average price. Of course, there would be a significant migration to Armani suits since they would be available at the same price as an outfit from the Gap. Operating the way electricity traditionally has worked, manufacturers would simply respond by manufacturing more Armani suits and the average price for all consumers would rise. This works great as long as you have a regulator who can force everyone to pay for the more expensive product (i.e., Armani suits) at an average price. But once you let anyone have direct access to buy directly from the Gap, at Gap prices, the whole system falls apart. We offer this story because while historically our regulatory mechanism has served up average prices, significant portions of the U.S. marketplace can now negotiate pricing directly with suppliers or can generate their own supply. This reality will continue to fundamentally change markets as more and more consumers are exposed to market-paced pricing or self-generation alternatives.

In many parts of the U.S. we now have business structures in which wholesale power is widely traded and where significant amounts of power are traded at market prices (as opposed to regulated prices). In others, the hold of the vertically integrated monopoly utility is still so strong that limited competition exists. Thus there are wide discrepancies across the U.S. in the maturity of wholesale markets. The same dichotomy exists to an even greater degree in retail markets. In a few states, most customers purchase power priced at market rates. In others, all customers still buy supply from a monopoly utility under traditional utility cost-of-service pricing. Many states have a mix where some customers are exposed to market prices and others aren't. And in some regions, the economics of distributed energy resources are making self-supply increasingly attractive. As you can see, market dynamics vary widely from region to region.

---

[1]Sally Hunt, *Making Competition Work in Electricity*, page 78.

U.S. REGIONAL MARKETPLACES			
Region	**Wholesale Competition**	**Retail Competition**	**DER Growth**
Northeast/Mid-Atlantic	High	High	Medium
Southeast	High in some areas, low in others	Low	Medium
Midwest	High	Medium, growing in some states	Medium
Rocky Mountain	Medium	Low	High
Northwest	Medium	Low	Low
California	High	Medium	High
Texas	High	High	Low

Supply and Demand

Because regulation has traditionally insulated customers from market pricing, electricity markets have not historically followed standard economic principles. The general paradigm in electric markets has been supply will be built to meet forecasted demand, regardless of cost. And demand is based on demographics, business activities, and weather patterns — again, regardless of cost issues. The other key factor about electricity demand is that time of use is critically important since peak demand drives much of the cost of the system, and capacity must be planned to meet the overall market peak even though that may occur only a few hours out of the year. Some utilities have moderated demand growth through demand side management (DSM) programs that encourage customers to enhance energy efficiency or move demands to off-peak periods. But in general, we have traditionally built power plants and transmission lines in step with forecasted demand increases.

In the long term, supply has historically been driven by demand forecasts. Once a utility's forecast indicates that a region's available supply is getting close to demand, the utility will request new resources in its integrated resource plan, regulators will approve either the construction or purchase of new resources, and voila, supply is increased. But in the short term, increasing supply is more difficult since it generally takes at least two years (and often much longer) to plan, design, permit, and build a new power plant. Thus there are really two sets of supply/demand issues to consider: long-term issues that relate to decisions to build new infrastructure and short-term issues that determine whether there is enough supply to cover customer needs for today, tomorrow, and this summer.

The way that the balance of supply and demand in a specific market region is evaluated is by looking at the reserve margin. The reserve margin is calculated as the total supply capacity in a region (supply can include generation plus available firm imports) minus the peak demand, divided by the peak demand. For instance, if a marketplace has 12,000 MW of supply and 10,000 MW of peak demand, the reserve margin would be: (12,000 — 10,000) ÷ 10,000 = 20%. Essentially, we are calculating how much extra supply is available to a given region. This is important for extreme weather situations or in the event any of the total supply should suddenly become unavailable. Although target reserve margins vary by region, a rule of thumb is that markets with reserve margins of less than 15% are considered tight. Those with margins between 15% and 20% are considered balanced, and those with margins greater than 20% are often considered oversupplied. Some regions now use a more sophisticated analysis that employs reliability simulations to determine what level of supply capacity is required so that daily system peak load is not likely to exceed available supply at any hour during the day more than once in a 10-year period.

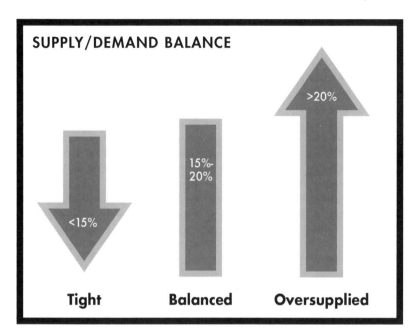

Short-term Supply and Demand

The short-term supply/demand balance is driven simply by projected demand and the supply available to meet it. The marketplace will generally look at this on a seasonal and monthly basis (since blocks of power are often traded and/or priced seasonally and monthly) and then again very closely in the day ahead (since this is when the system operator will schedule actual units and transmission lines). In the short term, demands are driven largely by weather (hot weather in summer driving cooling loads and cold weather in the winter driving heating loads) as well as business activity (often determined by the day of the week). Short-term supply is driven by the availability of generation units, transmission, firm power imports, and in some regions storage and flexible loads participating in supply markets.

A number of factors can impact unit availability including maintenance needs, environmental restrictions, fuel availability, and weather patterns (for hydro power and renewable resources such as wind and solar). In a competitive marketplace, additional factors such as contractual conditions, tariff provisions, and the behavior of market participants also come into play. On an hourly basis, unit availability is also impacted by start-up and ramp-up times. Units that haven't been started may not be available for a given hour if the time it takes to get them online safely is longer than the hour in which they are needed.

Transmission line availability is also an important factor when determining available supply. This is affected by weather (hot weather reduces capabilities), maintenance needs, and use of the lines by other market participants. If supply/demand is tight for a given day or hour both market prices and system reliability may be impacted.

Long-term Supply and Demand

In the longer term (greater than one year), demand is driven largely by demographics and business cycles. But also important are energy efficiency improvements and the growth rates of building electrification and electric vehicles. Long-term supply is affected by construction of new units and/or transmission lines, retirement of units, and, in some markets, availability of hydro power (driven by weather patterns) and growth of DERs. Construction of new units can be impacted by capital availability, regulatory decisions, environmental restrictions, willingness of buyers to sign long-term power purchase agreements, and market participants' perception of future profit opportunities (in competitive markets).

The Current Supply/Demand Situation in the U.S.

As of 2018, the supply/demand situation in the U.S. appeared stable (see map on page 179). Low demand growth in recent years due to increasing energy effi-

---

SHORT-TERM SUPPLY/DEMAND FACTORS

Supply

- Units with long start-up/ramp-up times
- Units out for maintenance
- Environmental permit restrictions
- Fuel availability
- Weather impacts on hydro and renewables
- Contractual and tariff provisions
- Actions of generation owners
- Transmission line availability
- Availability of firm import power

Demand

- Weather
- Business activity
- Availability of demand response

LONG-TERM SUPPLY/DEMAND FACTORS

Supply

- New generation/transmission construction
- Retirement of units
- Growth of DERs
- Long-term weather patterns

Demand

- Regional demographics
- Business cycles
- Growth of energy efficiency
- Electrification of buildings
- Growth of electric vehicles

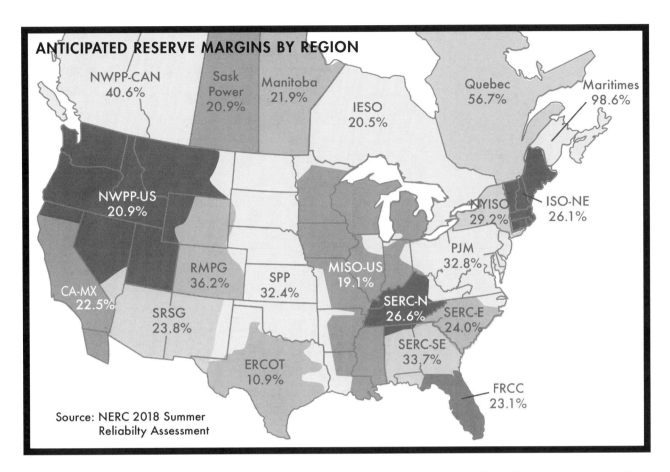

ANTICIPATED RESERVE MARGINS BY REGION

NWPP-CAN 40.6%

Sask Power 20.9%

Manitoba 21.9%

IESO 20.5%

Quebec 56.7%

Maritimes 98.6%

NWPP-US 20.9%

NYISO 29.2%

ISO-NE 26.1%

CA-MX 22.5%

RMPG 36.2%

SPP 32.4%

MISO-US 19.1%

PJM 32.8%

SRSG 23.8%

SERC-N 26.6%

SERC-E 24.0%

ERCOT 10.9%

SERC-SE 33.7%

FRCC 23.1%

Source: NERC 2018 Summer Reliabilty Assessment

ciency and slow growth in energy-consuming industries coupled with construction of natural gas and renewable generation resulted in sufficient reserve margins in all regions. Looking toward the future, the NERC 2018 Long-Term Reliability Assessment identified four regions with potential reliability challenges. Reserve margins in MISO, Ontario, and Texas are projected to be below reference reserve margins during some or all of the next five years and probabilistic models showed the potential for resource adequacy risks during non-peak hours in California. Key future factors associated with reliability include increasing reliance on gas generation in some regions, the impact of renewables and DERs on frequency and voltage management, the need for more flexible capacity to support growing renewable generation, expected rapid growth of distributed solar PV, growth of bulk power storage, and the potential for electric demand growth due to industrial loads and electric vehicles.

Pricing

Various factors influence the price of electricity at any given location at any point in time. Generally speaking, market-based prices are determined by market perceptions of the supply/demand balance. But in the electricity business things are more complex because some prices are set by regulation, not by the market. In this discussion we will consider only market-based pricing. The principles of regulated prices, which in the wholesale market are generally cost-of-service pricing, are covered in Section Ten. Market-based electricity prices are usually determined in one of two ways — through bilateral transactions or through centralized auctions. Bilateral transactions usually occur on the phone with two individuals negotiating and agreeing upon a price. For shorter transactions, the use of electronic exchanges such as the Intercontinental Exchange (ICE) has become common. Longer-term transactions are typically negotiated face to face. Until the advent of ISOs, bilateral trading encompassed virtually all market-based wholesale transactions, and this is still the predominant method for all pricing negotiated further ahead than the next day. Centralized auctions are run by ISOs for day-ahead and real-time energy markets, and in some regions for forward capacity markets. In the U.S., energy auctions run on the optimization methodology under integrated trading arrangements (for more details see Section Nine).

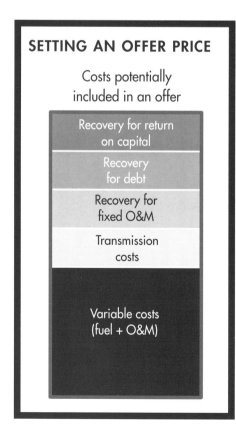

SETTING AN OFFER PRICE

Costs potentially
included in an offer

Recovery for return
on capital

Recovery
for debt

Recovery for
fixed O&M

Transmission
costs

Variable costs
(fuel + O&M)

Prices in bilateral transactions are driven by each organization's perception of supply and demand and what each party considers a fair price. Centralized auctions use marginal pricing that is determined by the price offer that would be accepted if the market required one more MW than the amount of supply required. Keep in mind that a fair offer may be greater than just the variable cost of operation. At some point in the year, owners of generation need to recover not only variable costs but also fixed costs, debt costs, and a margin of profit. Any such costs not received in capacity payments must be captured in energy markets. So during hours where supply is tight relative to demand, offers will be set not just to cover costs in those specific hours but also to recover the additional items mentioned above. Some peaking units may run only 50 to 100 hours for the entire year. This may not be significant if the unit owner has received a healthy capacity payment or is a utility that has put all the fixed costs and profit of its unit into a revenue requirement to be spread out over the year. It is very significant if that peaking unit is owned by a merchant generation company that has no guaranteed cost recovery.

Indexes and Trading Hubs

A basic requirement for a competitive commodity market is open price discovery. This means that all participants have access to information about the market price of electricity at specific locations. Indexes, compiled by buyers and sellers reporting trades and prices to an impartial third party, provide this information. Locations used for indexes are trading hubs, which are places where buyers and sellers commonly transfer ownership of electricity. Indexes are formulated in three ways. For regions with an ISO, data from ISO prices averaged across multiple hours can be used. For instance, it is common to use a peak price index that covers 16 hours across the day and an off-peak index that covers the eight hours across the night. Some ISOs provide pricing hubs that average regional prices to provide traders with

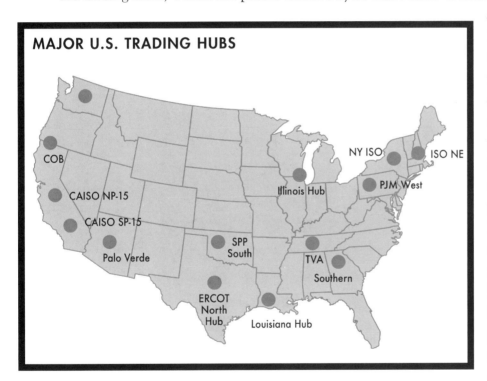

MAJOR U.S. TRADING HUBS

more liquid points. An example is The Midcontinent ISO (MISO), which provides the market with prices at eight pricing hubs: Indiana, Illinois, Michigan, Minnesota, Arkansas, Louisiana, Mississippi, and Texas. Indexes are also provided by the ICE for numerous trading points. Lastly, publications such as Platts Megawatt Daily provide indexes for key trading points based on deal reporting by key traders. To ensure the integrity of the indexes, FERC monitors markets and can enforce penalties for market manipulation. This is important because many market participants use indexed pricing in power purchase agreements.

Price Volatility

Price volatility, or the movement of price over time, is an inevitable fact of market-based electricity pricing. Since demands rise and fall significantly over the course of the day, power plants go online and offline for maintenance and other reasons, and output from wind and solar fluctuates, the hourly supply/demand equation is in constant flux. Prices can jump very quickly based on the cost of operation of the next power plant that must be turned on to satisfy an increase in demand (the marginal cost — see box below that discusses market price volatility).

Many observers say that price volatility in the electricity marketplace is the highest of any commodity that has ever been traded. It is very common on a normal day for electricity prices to go from $25/MWh to $60/MWh. And on a hot summer day where there are transmission line restrictions or units down for maintenance, a price of $150 or even $500/MWh would not be unexpected. In fact, we have even seen bilateral prices spike as high as a reported $7,500/MWh in one marketplace and real-time prices in ERCOT exceeded $9,000/MWh for brief periods in the summer of 2019! Price volatility is made more extreme by the fact that most electric markets do not have much in the way of a demand response to price. Since many customers are being charged average rates that only change once a year, they are oblivious to high wholesale prices — even at a price of $500/MWh (five times higher than a common residential rate). This extreme volatility has resulted in the need for sophisticated risk management techniques which we will discuss in the following section.

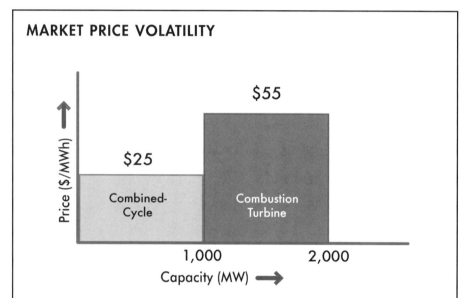

MARKET PRICE VOLATILITY

In the graph above, the marginal cost of generation in the marketplace is $25/MWh as long as demand does not reach 1,000 MW. Once demand hits 1,000 MW, the marginal cost becomes $55. And in an ISO market where everyone gets paid the marginal price, the ISO price for all power becomes $55 even if demand has only gone up from 999 MW to 1,000 MW. This is why price volatility is to be expected.

The Importance of Gas Prices in Many Electric Markets

In many electric markets in the U.S., natural gas generation is the marginal resource during many hours of the year. And since marginal gas generators cannot forecast which hours of a month they may be dispatched, it is difficult for these generators to lock in fixed gas prices (since gas marketers will typically not offer a fixed price unless the buyer is willing to commit to a fixed volume). Instead, generators often buy gas supply in spot markets. This means that the generators' cost of generating electricity will vary in direct proportion to gas market prices. In such markets, the price of electricity in any given hour can often be forecast fairly accurately by taking the market price of gas and multiplying it by the heat rate of the marginal unit. And during times of extreme weather, gas prices tend to spike. The result is often significant spikes in electricity prices until the weather event ends.

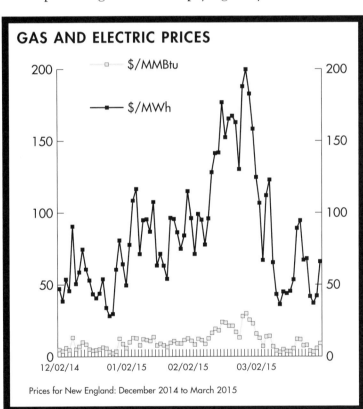

GAS AND ELECTRIC PRICES

Prices for New England: December 2014 to March 2015

The Wholesale Market

A wholesale electric market refers to the platform where transactions occur between two parties, neither of which is the ultimate consumer of the electricity. In many parts of the U.S. a fairly robust wholesale market has evolved. Characteristics of a highly competitive market include many buyers and sellers (a liquid market), prices determined by market conditions, price transparency, no individual or group of companies with market power, and no barriers to transfer of goods (i.e., no issues with transmission access or capacity and no regulatory restrictions on transactions). These conditions exist to a degree in various regional markets in the U.S., and competitive wholesale marketplaces continue to grow in most regions of the country.

Services in the wholesale marketplace include energy (kWh), capacity (kW), transmission rights, and financial risk management. Participants include utilities, federal power

WHOLESALE SERVICES		
Service Provided	**Service Provider**	**Service Consumer**
Energy (MWh)	Merchant generators and IPPs Utilities Federal power agencies ISOs Wholesale marketers DER aggregators	Utilities ISOs Wholesale marketers Retail marketers Large end users
Capacity (MW)	Merchant generators and IPPs Utilities Federal power agencies ISOs Wholesale marketers DER aggregators	Utilities ISOs Wholesale marketers Retail marketers
Ancillary Services	Merchant generators and IPPs Utilities Federal power agencies ISOs	Utilities ISOs Retail marketers
Transmission Rights	Utilities Transmission companies ISOs	Merchant generators Utilities Wholesale marketers Retail marketers
Financial Risk Management	Financial companies ISOs Wholesale marketers	Merchant generators Utilities Wholesale marketers Retail marketers Large end users

13

agencies, merchant generators and IPPs, wholesale marketers, retail marketers, ISOs, transmission companies, and financial services providers. These services are discussed in greater detail on the following pages.

Energy and Generation Capacity

Energy sales refer to the sale of electricity that will be generated and transmitted on the grid to the point of sale. In the wholesale marketplace this is measured in MWh. Capacity sales refer to the sale of a right to call on generation capacity if needed or an obligation for a generator to offer supply in an ISO market. Capacity is measured in MW. While energy sales are generally priced simply in $/MWh, some capacity sales have a two-part price: a $/MW component that is paid for the reservation of capacity

MARKET TURMOIL

In the period 2000–2002 electricity markets were hit with a number of perturbations that threw them into turmoil. Events that occurred include:

- The California energy crisis, which raised wholesale prices to unprecedented levels throughout the western grid.

- The bankruptcy of Enron, the largest trader of electricity in North America, followed by bankruptcies of other large wholesale traders and merchant generators including Mirant, NRG, and PG&E National Energy Group. Others avoided bankruptcy but suffered severe financial stress.

- Revelations that numerous companies had engaged in questionable accounting and other business practices.

- Exposure of widespread abuse of tariff conditions, power plant availability rules, and index reporting practices that allowed some wholesale market participants to drive prices to high levels and apparently earn huge profits at the expense of consumers.

These events led to a general questioning and mistrust of those engaged in electricity trading and marketing and, combined with a drop in power prices that caught many merchant generators with inadequate cash flows, led to a huge crash in market values of many companies. A number of entities that had been the largest market players in the wholesale business were forced to try to sell assets to stave off bankruptcy and were no longer viable market participants. Over the next few years a number of assets changed hands, new participants emerged, and trading continued. After all, trading must go on. Owners of power plants must find customers and Load Serving Entities must find sources of supply. So anywhere the vertical utility can't serve 100% of its loads with its own generation, there will always be some form of electricity trading.

whether it is used or not, and an additional $/MWh component that is paid if the unit is dispatched. Capacity sales in an ISO market are single price based on $/MW. The price paid for energy if the unit is dispatched is set by the market.

Two markets exist for energy: forward markets (which are commitments for a time in the future) and spot markets (which are commitments to deliver energy on the same day or for the day following the transactions). Capacity markets tend to be only forward. Within each category there are numerous types of contracts that are common.

Forward Energy Markets

Common contract structures for forward energy markets include:

- Full-requirements agreement — A full-requirements agreement obligates the seller to provide all the energy required for the buyer. For a small utility, a full-requirements agreement would replace the need to own its own generation. Common users of full-requirements agreements are small municipal or co-op utilities that contract with a public power agency or with a federal power authority. Full-requirements agreements may also be used by end-use customers who wish to contract with a marketer to provide for all their electricity needs.

- Partial-requirements agreement — A partial-requirements agreement obligates the seller to provide a fixed amount of energy (MWh) to the buyer.

- Firm power — This means that the seller has provided a fixed amount of energy and has reserved transmission to deliver the power to the buyer. Firm power usually must be paid for whether or not the buyer takes it.

- Life-of-the-plant — This is an agreement between an IPP and a utility where the utility contracts for the capacity of the unit for as long as the unit is in service. Under this contract the utility would normally have the rights to dispatch the unit. This is used as an alternative to the utility building the unit itself.

- Pooling agreements — These are agreements among multiple owners of generation and buyers of energy that agree to put their assets into a pool and have them operated for overall optimization of the group.

- Tolling agreement or heat-rate agreement — This is an agreement between an energy buyer and a power plant. The buyer agrees to provide the necessary fuel (usually natural gas) and to take the energy produced. The power plant is paid a fee for running the unit to convert the fuel into electricity. The plant must also agree to run the unit in such a manner as to meet a minimum heat rate and availability.

- Balance of the month — An agreement to provide energy for the remaining days in the current month.

- Non-firm power — This is energy that is sold on an as-available basis. There are no commitments as to availability of capacity and/or transmission and no commitment on the part of the buyer to purchase the power if she does not want it.

- Peak power — An agreement to buy/sell energy for the peak period. Unlike elsewhere in the industry, the wholesale market uses peak to refer to the 16 hours between 7 a.m. and 11 p.m. Much of the country trades 5 x 16 blocks, meaning the 5 weekdays and 16 hours per day. The western regions often trade 6 x 16 blocks that add in Saturday.

- Off-peak power — An agreement to buy/sell energy for the hours not defined as peak (see above).

- Round-the-clock — An agreement to buy/sell energy for all 24 hours of a day.

Day-ahead and Real-time Energy Markets

Spot markets include day-ahead sales (energy being sold for the following day) and sales for energy to be used on the day of the sale. Sales for the same day are commonly termed hour-ahead (for the next full hour) or real-time energy. Imbalance energy is energy bought or sold by the system operator to keep the system in balance within a specific hour. Day-ahead and hour-ahead spot market sales may be bilateral transactions that take place between two private market participants or they may be transactions that occur through an ISO auction.

As we discussed in Section Seven, system operators must ensure sufficient ancillary services including AGC, various categories of reserves, flexible ramp, voltage support, and blackstart. These services are commonly traded in non-ISO wholesale markets when there are numerous smaller utilities and are traded through ISO markets in regions with an ISO. In regions with no ISO, ancillary services are traded bilaterally or are provided under FERC-approved Open Access Transmission (OAT) tariffs. In ISO markets, services including AGC, reserves, and flexible ramp are provided through hourly ISO markets in the day ahead. Voltage support and blackstart are typically acquired by the ISO from generators in annual bilateral agreements.

Transmission Rights

Transmission rights are used by generators and/or marketers to deliver power to a point of sale. Given the current state of the transmission infrastructure, rights to use transmission can make or break any given transaction. The way that transmission rights are made available varies depending on the market structure and trading arrangements (see Section Nine). Under the wheeling method, types of rights include long-term firm transmission (usually held only by utilities and under long-term contracts), wheeling firm transmission (firm transmission made available on a transaction-by-transaction basis under the utility OAT tariffs), and wheeling non-firm transmission. Once a market has transformed to an ISO marketplace, transmission rights transition to a transmission congestion model. Under this model, transmission is allocated on an hour-by-hour basis in the spot market with congestion costs applying to users of any congested paths. To hedge against the financial uncertainty associated with congestion costs, ISOs often offer financial transmission rights (FTRs). FTRs are allocated or auctioned off to the marketplace and provide a fixed-price guarantee associated with use of a certain transmission path.

Financial Services

Generators, marketers, and utilities holding assets or contracts and/or needing to purchase future supply that is subject to market fluctuations may turn to financial markets to hedge some or all of the price risk. Common products include price swaps (exchanging variable price risk for a fixed price) and options (used to create price floors and ceilings that reduce risk of price fluctuations). We will take a closer look at these concepts in Section Fourteen.

The Retail Market

Retail markets refer to transactions between the supplier and the end user of electricity services. Retail markets are split between those where retail access is permitted by regulation and those where utilities remain monopoly suppliers. Unlike the wholesale market that is extremely sensitive to price considerations, portions of the retail market are often more sensitive to service and relationships than to price. Many smaller end-use customers see electricity as a fundamental necessity for their homes and businesses but cannot afford to focus too much on day-to-day transactions. For this reason, they are more likely to pay a premium to receive good service.

RETAIL SERVICES		
Service Provided	**Service Provider**	**Service Consumer**
Supply	Utilities Wholesale marketers Retail marketers Aggregators	End-use customers
Value-added Services	Utilities Retail marketers ESCOs	End-use customers

In the U.S., large consumers of electricity are often the first customers calling for regulatory reforms to allow them to choose their suppliers and quickly take advantage of supply options once they are available. Smaller customers as a whole are much more reluctant to switch suppliers given their uncertainty about the level of benefits associated with switching. The amount of load served by competitive suppliers has grown slowly but steadily in recent years in the U.S. In 2003, approximately 240 million MWh were served by competitive suppliers. By 2017, this had increased to 800 million MWh, which is about 21% of total U.S. loads. As markets mature in states with retail choice it is expected that the amount of load served by non-utility suppliers will continue to grow.

Another type of retail access that has grown in recent years is called community aggregation. Under this method, government entities such as cities or counties are allowed to take over the supply function for citizens who choose to opt in to their offerings. This is different than a full municipal utility, because the existing distribution utility continues to be responsible for distribution of the power, with the community simply taking over the function of acquiring supply.

Services in the retail market center on the provision of energy (kWh) and other related services. Other important services may include energy efficiency, demand side management, clean power, power reliability, power quality, and energy information. These may be provided by a utility or any number of competitive suppliers. These services are discussed in greater detail below.

Utility Retail Services

Retail services provided by utilities are defined in the utility's tariffs and must be approved by the regulatory commission. Services are associated with specific customer classes such as residential, small commercial, large commercial, and industrial. All customers take utility distribution services whether or not they have access to competitive suppliers. Larger customers tend to have two-part rates that include a demand charge and an energy charge while smaller customers usually pay only energy charges. Most customers pay a monthly customer charge, which is a fixed amount per account based on the customer class. Energy and demand charges may be fixed throughout the year or may vary by season (summer and winter rates are common). For some customers, time-of-use rates may be applied where rates are different at different times of the day (for instance, a higher rate might be charged from 3 p.m. to 8 p.m. and a lower rate for the rest of the day). In some regions time-of-use rates and demand charges are being extended to smaller customers and may eventually apply to all customers.

TYPICAL UTILITY SERVICES

- Residential
- Residential Experimental Time-of-use (TOU)
- Residential Multi-unit
- Small Commercial
- Commercial Demand Metered
- Commercial Demand Metered TOU
- Industrial TOU
- Industrial TOU Curtailable
- Agriculture
- Electric Vehicle Charging
- Street Lighting

Larger customers often have the option of choosing curtailable rates, real-time prices (which vary based on the market price), or taking service at higher voltage (primary or transmission-level service). Utilities may also offer value-added services centered on energy efficiency or demand side management incentives that are designed to reduce overall peak loads and thus hold down costs for all customers. Utilities may also offer assistance with power reliability or power quality issues and in many regions offer green power options.

Competitive Retail Services

In regions where direct access is permitted, customers have the option of acquiring supply from competitive suppliers known as retail marketers (large customers sometimes buy from suppliers that focus mainly on wholesale trading since these users buy in large volumes, so you may also hear it said they are buying from wholesale marketers). For larger customers, offerings generally center on price and/or integrated services. In today's market where there are large price uncertainties, a typical pricing methodology is to offer specific kW blocks of power at a fixed price, with additional usage priced at a market index rate. In some cases suppliers may offer ceilings and floors for the portions priced at market rates. Integrated service offerings tie energy efficiency, demand side management, and/or multiple fuel services into one package and are attractive to customers who are not large enough to have in-house energy expertise and larger customers who choose to outsource this function. Small commercial and residential customers are more apt to buy full-requirements power (power covering all their needs) at fixed prices that are adjusted periodically to account for market changes. As retail markets mature, marketers are beginning to offer multiple service options to residential customers including bundling TV, internet, or other utilities and even assistance with rooftop solar or electric vehicles.

ESCO and Other Energy Services

Energy services companies, known as ESCOs, provide important services in either regulated or competitive retail markets. ESCOs work directly with end users to help them minimize their energy costs. Services include bill evaluation, energy efficiency, demand side management, usage monitoring, appliance maintenance, distributed generation, and, in competitive markets, choice of suppliers and supply contract negotiation assistance. An additional important service offered is assistance with power reliability or power quality needs. This may come from an ESCO or an engineering or equipment firm.

What you will learn:

- How various market participants create profits

- How profits are created under cost-of-service and incentive ratemaking

- Key skills for creating profits

- What risk management is and why it's important

 - How market participants manage risk using physical and financial instruments

- The difference between hedging and speculating

- How Value at Risk (VAR) is used to measure risk levels

SECTION FOURTEEN: MAKING MONEY AND MANAGING RISK

It goes without saying that the ultimate goal for all market participants is to make money. But since large portions of the electric industry continue to be dominated by regulated monopolies, the basic concepts that apply to making money do not necessarily apply to all the entities we have studied. Nor is there always a strong incentive to develop products and services solely focused on customer desires (since much of the ability to make money for a regulated entity is determined by regulators, not customers). The electric industry is further complicated by a unique mixture of regulated and non-regulated entities, as well as the variation of regulation and market structures from state to state and region to region. Thus it is critically important to understand the differing profit motivations of various market participants and how each makes money.

KEY SKILLS FOR PROFITABLE BUSINESSES		
Non-regulated	**Traditional Regulation**	**Incentive Regulation**
• Marketing/pricing • Asset management • Financial management • Customer service • Billing • Credit and collections • Efficient operations • Information technology	• Regulatory/government relations • Expense containment • Asset expansion • Service reliability • Reliable operations • Safe operations	• Purchasing • Expense containment • Productivity enhancement • Marketing/pricing • Information technology • Achieving service standards • Asset management

As we study the various ways in which market participants make money, we must also consider the inherent risks involved at all levels of the business. When we talk about risk, we mean the possibility that earnings will be lower than projected or lower than the market will support at the time products or services are delivered. Until the 1990s, a section on risk in a book on the electric industry would have been very short. With all aspects of the industry regulated, the biggest risk a utility faced was regulatory risk — the risk that regulators would lower its rate of return or otherwise rule in such a

decoupling makes utility earnings streams less risky and can encourage utilities to support energy efficiency programs.

How a Utility Makes Money — Incentive Regulation

As the electric business restructures, regulators are likely to look at new ways of reforming the regulatory process. In some areas, traditional cost-of-service regulation is being supplemented with incentive regulation, which creates shareholder incentives for utilities to lower costs and reduce rates or to achieve other regulatory goals. As market-based rates become common in the wholesale marketplace, it will be harder for a utility to prosper under traditional regulation. Any time market rates are lower than the utility's cost of energy, intervenors will claim the utility performed unreasonably and that shareholders should bear some of the excess costs. Thus many utilities may prefer to accept the risks and rewards of incentive regulation. Under incentive regulation, utilities can increase profits by achieving or exceeding standards or market-based targets set by the regulator. For more information on incentive regulation, please see the discussion in Section Ten.

How Unregulated Market Participants Make Money

Unlike regulated entities, other market participants' profitability is driven by the harsh realities of market dynamics. These include whether the participant is selling a service that the market is willing to buy, whether the participant is able to provide that service at a cost that still provides a reasonable profit given the price the market is willing to pay, and whether the participant is able to deliver the service after the product has been sold. In a volatile electricity marketplace, many entities have discovered that shareholder losses and even bankruptcy can be a heartbeat away! For example, generation owners may find that prices are too low to provide a profit on units that need to repay debt. And some retail marketers have guaranteed fixed prices to customers only to see the market cost of supply rise significantly. As the electricity business matures, strategies for profitability have begun to resemble strategies used by other competitive industries such as airlines and consumer product marketing.

Risk Management

Recent events in the electricity business make it very clear that no matter how a market participant makes money, the levels of risk encountered in the marketplace are so extreme that companies can go from apparent profitability to insolvency in the course of a few short months. All market participants must actively and thoroughly manage

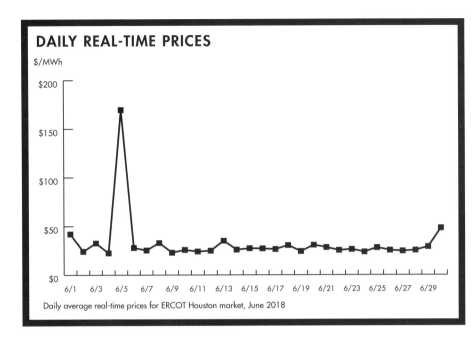

DAILY REAL-TIME PRICES

$/MWh

Daily average real-time prices for ERCOT Houston market, June 2018

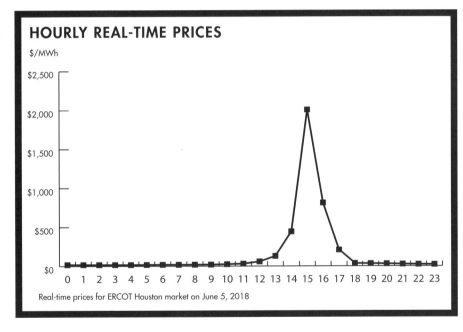

HOURLY REAL-TIME PRICES

$/MWh

Real-time prices for ERCOT Houston market on June 5, 2018

their risks at all times. If they aren't doing this, they are placing their shareholders' investment in severe jeopardy.

One key reason for the need for risk management is that electricity prices have proven to be highly volatile at times. The graph to the left shows the daily average real-time price for ERCOT Houston for the month of June 2018. For all of the days of the month but one, prices were below $44/MWh. But on June 5th, the average price spiked to $169.52/MWh. The next day, average prices dropped to $27.86. What can cause such volatility? The answer is as simple as supply and demand. On the 5th, temperatures were abnormally hot and demand soared late in the afternoon and early evening. Meanwhile, transmission into Houston was constrained meaning supply from cheaper regions was unavailable to serve all Houston loads. And to make matters worse, weather conditions reduced the availability of wind power. The result was that expensive peaker units were required to serve the loads during just a few hours that day. The extremely high prices during these hours pushed the daily average price to increase by a factor of five compared to the previous day. But once loads dropped just a little, these units were no longer needed and the prices rapidly decreased. While such price spikes benefit a market participant with available generation, they can result in a huge loss for an unprepared market participant who is forced to buy supply during these time periods.

Because the U.S. has separate regional grids that often have transmission constraints between them, prices will vary significantly in different regions. And unlike the natural gas industry where there is relatively strong correlation between prices in various regions, correlation between regions without transmission interconnections is often non-existent in the electric business.

The risk that we have been discussing so far is price risk. This is just one of many risks that are currently inherent in the electric marketplace:

- Price Risk — The risk that prices will move in the opposite direction to what the participant desires. This risk can be even more extreme for generation owners who not only face the risk of electric market pricing, but also the risk of price movement in their fuel supply.

- Volume risk — The risk that a customer does not use as much or uses more electricity than the supplier anticipated. This risk can result in unexpected spot purchases and/or sales or unexpected balancing charges.

- Transmission risk — The risk that a transmission path necessary to complete your transaction will be congested, resulting in unexpected transmission congestion costs or the need to buy replacement power at a higher price.

- Counterparty risk — The risk that any party you do business with will not honor its commitments.

- Execution risk — The risk that someone within your company fails to execute a transaction properly (e.g., a contract is not signed or a contractual condition not met).

- Tariff or regulatory risk — The risk that the regulator will change the rules applying to a business transaction after you have signed the contract.

- Operational risk — The risk that an asset you counted on fails to operate as expected.

Choices for Managing Risk

Risks are managed by developing and implementing a thorough internal risk management program, which includes measuring risk levels on a daily or hourly basis, structuring of physical transactions, use of financial instruments, and careful management of counterparty relationships. Following are descriptions of some of the most common risk management techniques used in the electric industry today.

Physical Risk Management

A physical deal is an agreement to buy or sell electric supply or transmission rights. Depending on the existing market position of the parties, physical risk management can include fixed pricing, pricing tied to market indexes, pricing with ceilings and floors, and selling physical blocks (meaning that the seller is providing a specific amount of kWh so that there is no risk of having to go out and buy more power on the spot market to supply the customer). Other means of physical risk management include setting up alternate contracts with other suppliers, having a right to call on generation capacity at a specific price, tolling agreements (whereby the buyer has the rights to use generation capacity at a specific price and is responsible for supplying the fuel), fixed pricing on fuel contracts, and building a portfolio of deals so that any single deal does not expose a large portion of a company's finances. One last means of physical risk management is owning assets, including generation and fuel assets and/or signing long-term fixed price contracts to utilize assets owned by another party.

Most marketers or generators would prefer to make only transactions that are structured in such a way that profits are locked in before the contract is signed. The problem is that such a requirement can severely limit the number of transactions available. Another problem with physical deals is that they can be difficult to unwind (or get out of) if the market changes. Thus market participants often depend on a combination of physical deal structures and more liquid financial instruments to manage risk.

FINANCIAL INSTRUMENTS

Futures — A future is a supply contract between a buyer and seller where the buyer is obligated to take delivery and the seller is obligated to provide delivery of a fixed amount of commodity at a predetermined price and location at a specific time. Although futures can result in physical delivery, they are usually used as financial instruments by simply trading them back at or near the close of the trading period.

Options — An option is similar to a future but differs in that it is the right, but not the obligation, to sell or purchase an amount of power.

Swaps — A swap is a contract that pays/charges depending on price relationships between a market index and a fixed price. Swaps are used to exchange fixed for floating prices or vice versa.

OTC Instruments — Also known as derivatives, OTC instruments are more flexible than futures or options since they are not traded on an exchange and can be designed as desired by the two parties involved.

Financial Risk Management

The use of financial instruments to manage risks has been common in commodity industries for decades. Financial instruments provide a means for market participants to shift risk without actually trading a physical commodity. Instruments used to do this include exchange-based futures and options, ISO-based financial transmission rights (FTRs), and over-the-counter (OTC) derivatives. Exchange-based instruments are specific defined contracts that trade on a central exchange like the CME Group (formerly NYMEX) or Intercontinental Exchange (ICE), while OTC instruments are simply contracts between two private parties.

Trading volume, or liquidity, of risk management tools grew relatively slowly in the electricity industry during the initial years of deregulation. Reasons for this lack of liquidity include the lack of price correlation between regional hubs due to lack of transmission interconnections, the limited amount of power traded in some wholesale markets due to continued dominance of vertically integrated utilities, and the wide variation of power demand and prices across the day. However, the availability of risk management products has grown significantly in recent years in the competitive wholesale markets. Both CME and ICE offer services that match buyers and sellers for various products at numerous hubs. Products include futures, swaps, location spreads, and options. Also, each ISO offers financial instruments that allow parties to hedge the risk of transmission congestion costs for specific transmission paths. These are commonly called Financial Transmission Rights or FTRs, although different terms are used by different ISOs. Numerous financial services companies also offer OTC products.

Financial instruments are used by wholesale market participants to cover the risk of price fluctuations. For instance, a marketer may have a contract to sell a block of power to an end-use customer at a fixed price but may be buying power at a market index. Rather than carry the risk of rising market prices, the marketer can lock in a margin by swapping the floating price (the indexed supply purchase) for a fixed price. Generators may also use instruments to lock in fixed revenues and are likely to be active in the fuel-hedging markets to reduce their risks associated with coal, petroleum, and/or natural gas price fluctuations.

Speculation versus Hedging

To understand the use of financial instruments, you must clearly understand the difference between hedging and speculation. Hedgers reduce risk by paying a third party to assume that risk, much like a homeowner pays an insurance company to assume the risk of rebuilding her house in the event of a fire. Speculators, on the other hand, take

A SIMPLE EXAMPLE OF HEDGING

You are a small merchant generator with a contract to sell 10 MW of power with a fixed price of $32.00/MWh to an end user for the month of April. Your generator is fueled by natural gas and you are currently buying your gas supply at a floating monthly index price. Thus you are at risk that gas prices may increase to the point where you are unable to generate power at or below the fixed sales price. To hedge your risk, you might do the following:

- Natural gas prices in your area for the current month are $3.50/Dth which, given the heat rate of your unit, is equivalent to a generation cost of $28.00/MWh. But you are unable to lock in a gas price for the month of April that you find attractive.

- To cover your gas price risk, you buy NYMEX April futures to match the volume of gas you need to generate the 10 MW of power you have sold. NYMEX April futures are selling for $3.06/Dth.

- When the end of the month approaches, you go into the market to buy gas for delivery to your power plant. You discover that gas prices have risen and you must pay $4.10/Dth to acquire the gas supply. You also see that NYMEX futures for April have gone up to $3.55/Dth. You buy the physical gas and sell the futures.

- Your purchase of gas at $4.10/Dth results in your generating electricity at a cost of $32.80/MWh and selling it at $32.00/MWh — not a good way to generate shareholder profits!

- But with your hedging, you will sell your gas futures at a profit, thus covering your physical loss:

Date	Cash Deal	Futures Deal
March 7	Sold electricity at $32.00/MWh	Bought gas futures at the equivalent cost of $24.48/MWh
March 26	Bought gas at the equivalent cost of $32.80/MWh	Sold gas futures at the equivalent price of $28.40/MWh
Profit/Loss	($0.80/MWh) loss	$3.92/MWh gain

After closing out all your transactions, your net gain on the sale is $3.12/MWh. Your customer, by the way, is also pleased with your performance. Assuming natural gas generation is on the margin, it is likely electric market prices rose as well and your customer bought power at a below-market price.

on risk in the hopes of making money (for instance, if the insurance company takes in more money than it pays out in all of its fire claims, it has speculated successfully on the risk of its customers' fire losses).

On one side of a financial transaction, there is a party attempting to hedge risk. On the other side is a financial services company hoping to profit by taking on the risk of price volatility. This is achieved by charging a fee for the service, building a margin into any price guarantee, and/or designing a portfolio of transactions so the financial services company can profit by being a middleman between parties. For instance, if you were going to offer a product guaranteeing price, you might project the expected price level, add in $5/MWh to cover the risk, and add a couple more dollars per MWh for profit. It is critical for both sides of a transaction to carefully track what risk has been assigned to what party and who is hedging versus speculating. Most of the negative stories about use of financial derivatives have occurred because firms were speculating and misjudged the level of risk or because firms thought they were hedging but did not properly understand the level of risk to which they remained exposed.

Hedging Techniques

Risks can be hedged in a variety of ways. Following are examples of four common techniques used in the electricity business:

- Buying or selling at a fixed price — This requires no financial instruments as long as prices are fixed on both sides of a transaction. For instance, a marketer may agree to sell electricity to a Texas end user for one year at a price of $52/MWh. Because the price is fixed for the end user, that customer has no price risk for the length of the agreement. While the marketer has no price risk on the sale side of the transaction, she may be open to extreme risk if she hasn't locked in adequate electric supply at a specific price to cover the deal. Thus, she will attempt to find a generator willing to provide the supply at a fixed price.

- Using over-the-counter derivatives — Many market participants use OTC derivatives for financial risk management. These instruments, offered by financial services companies, banks, and some marketers mimic many of the features of the centralized futures/options market but at different locations and under different terms. An example of an OTC derivative would be a price ceiling at the California-Oregon Border (COB). In this example, a bank guarantees a marketer that he will never pay more than $65/MWh for the summer months. If the price exceeds $65, the bank will compensate him for the difference between the higher price and the $65 ceiling. Another common OTC derivative is known as a price swap. Here someone holding an electric supply asset (either generation or a contract to buy electricity) subject to market price risk may "swap" the price risk to a financial services company and instead receive a fixed price. OTC derivatives can be extremely varied and the products offered can differ widely. Margins and transaction costs are often high since the financial services company is taking on substantial risk given the volatility of the electric industry.

- Using financial transmission rights (FTRs) — If a generator or a marketer must use a path that is sometimes congested to deliver power to a customer, the supplier is at risk for transmission congestion costs. These can quickly turn a profitable transaction into a loss. One way for the supplier to hedge this risk is to buy FTRs from the ISO. Each ISO has its own procedures for offering FTRs, but the general process is that financial rights associated with a specific path are auctioned periodically. The winner of the auction then has usage of that path for a guaranteed cost, regardless of congestion costs. The supplier can then build this cost into his transaction pricing and is no longer exposed to this risk.

- Laying off counterparty risk — Over the last couple of years, a number of parties heavily involved in electric trading have either gone into bankruptcy or have become financially insolvent. This has resulted in contracts that have not been honored. Market participants now pay close attention to counterparty risk before entering into a transaction. Means of handling this risk include refusing to do business with parties that don't have a solid financial rating, putting provisions into the contract that allow for termination of the agreement if the counterparty fails to maintain defined standards of financial strength, requiring the party to put up a significant portion of the contract value in a letter of credit or escrow payment, and trading through a clearing exchange such as ICE or CME that includes provisions to compensate parties for counterparty losses.

Value at Risk

Whatever techniques are used to manage risk, it is critical for management of a company to actively measure the aggregate risk level it has incurred on at least a daily, if not an hourly, basis. The risk that is measured is the risk to the company's expected earnings stream if certain movements in market price or other detrimental events were to occur. This aggregate risk is measured by creating a "book" that shows all physical and financial positions and using this information to estimate the earnings impact of various potential price movements. Procedures must also be in place to catch accidental execution mistakes or unauthorized actions of employees who may be trading outside of the guidelines given by management. We are all too familiar with the potential for huge impacts caused by failures in risk management.

A common way of measuring aggregate risk is called Value at Risk (VAR). In industry jargon, VAR can be described as "an estimate of a portfolio's potential for loss due to market movements, using standard statistical techniques and an estimate of future market volatility." In layman's terms, VAR is a calculation that attempts to assess how much total risk a company has taken on over any given period of time.

Unfortunately, VAR is an imperfect means of quantifying actual risk. To calculate VAR, an assumption is made as to what level of market volatility will be experienced and then a level of statistical certainty is chosen (often 95%). Given a 95% certainty, your actual Value at Risk will theoretically exceed your calculation 18 days out of the year (5% of the time). And if one of those days is a day when electricity prices spike well above expected levels, you can lose a lot of money quickly! In reality, one number cannot adequately reflect the complex risks encountered in today's marketplace. Thus it is always important to understand that the levels of risk in the marketplace are inherently high, and no means of analysis or use of risk management techniques can fully hedge all risks.

Despite this caveat, VAR is useful for a number of purposes:

- Quickly quantifying risk associated with a specific transaction.

- Comparing risk associated with expected return for alternative transactions.

- Quantifying risk across a portfolio of transactions (rather than looking at each transaction individually).

- Evaluating overall corporate risk profiles.

- Setting limits on allowed risk either by specific trader, specific business unit, or corporate-wide.

As the industry has become experienced with risks associated with energy markets, new more complex analysis tools that go beyond simple VAR have been developed. It is likely that in the years to come, risk management techniques will continue to evolve.

What you will learn:

- How the generation, transmission, distribution, system operations, and retail sales sectors may evolve

- A vision for a sustainable energy future

SECTION FIFTEEN: THE FUTURE OF THE ELECTRICITY BUSINESS

As we have seen in this book, the electricity industry has gone through radical change since the mid-1990s. Some regions, once dominated by vertical utilities that controlled all aspects of the business, have now become competitive markets with robust wholesale marketplaces and active competition for sales to end-use customers. Other regions remain dominated by strong vertical utilities and have felt little of the turbulent marketplace changes. But with falling prices for renewable energy, the growth of distributed energy resources, and new customer expectations all markets are poised for another wave of dramatic change.

Technology evolution also continues to drive rapid change in the electricity industry. Development of natural gas combined-cycle turbine technology led to a rise of gas-fired generation that, coupled with falling gas prices driven by advancing gas drilling techniques, has resulted in the closure of numerous coal-fired units and even some nuclear units. Meanwhile development of wind and solar technologies has driven dramatic growth in renewable generation in some areas. Price reductions and technology advancements have resulted in grid batteries becoming a practicable resource. And growth of low-cost communications technology and electronic metering has led to increasing capability for flexible loads to participate in markets. Many believe that technology advancements along with market changes will result in a dramatically different electric grid within the next decade.

The one thing we can be sure of is that the electric business will continue to see frequent change. While no one can predict a precise course of events, a look at ongoing trends and past experience in other businesses might give us some indication of what to expect.

A Review of Market Changes

In the mid-1990s, all sectors of the industry were vertically integrated in monopoly utilities and virtually all pricing was based on a regulated cost-of-service model. This is still true in some regions of the U.S. But in other areas including the Northeast, the

Midwest, Texas, and portions of the Southeast and the West, wholesale competition is well established.

We have seen the beginnings of competitive generation in virtually all areas, first from power generated by QFs and then from merchant generators. Many regions of the country have turned power control functions over to ISOs that use a market-based approach to acquiring reliability services and allocating access to transmission. Some areas have seen the utilities divest of generation, and, in a few cases, even transmission. We are beginning to see transmission-only companies emerge, and these entities may build much of the next wave of transmission infrastructure. By 2017, over 21% of electric load was acquiring supply through competitive suppliers rather than from the monopoly utility. Interestingly, although reports of market manipulation and energy company financial struggles dominated the headlines during this time of evolution, average retail rates fell during most of the restructuring period. Perhaps heralding the next wave of market change, the capacity of distributed solar generation in the U.S. more than tripled between 2014 and 2018, and is forecast by NERC to more than double again to over 30 GW by 2023.

The Future of the Generation Sector

The merchant generation business has proven to be extremely volatile. During the late 1990s and early 2000s a large amount of generation was built and much of it was financed with high levels of debt. Many areas of the country ended up with excess capacity thanks to an economic slowdown and a slowdown in restructuring that restricted opportunities for competitive generation in some areas. The result was many merchant generators found themselves struggling to stay in business. Restructuring of generation ownership and financing followed. In some areas this included utilities buying formerly competitive units to bring them into rate base, while in others new well-financed generation companies bought up assets at a significant discount to their cost of construction. As demands continued to grow and construction of power plants slowed, merchant generation in the mid-2000s again became a profitable business. But with the economic downturn in 2008 resulting in falling demand, lower market prices, and tight credit, many merchant generators again struggled. And recently, low natural gas prices and additions in wind power have resulted in further squeezing of generator margins. Many owners of less efficient coal units and even some nuclear units have found they can no longer compete in the marketplace and have retired these units from service.

As of 2019, growth in renewables is a dominant factor in many regions of the U.S. In 2018, about 60% of new generation built in the U.S. (including utility-scale and distributed generation) was renewable, almost all either wind or solar. While renewable generation got much of its initial growth through state renewable portfolios and tax benefits, dropping costs have now made renewables cost competitive with traditional fossil fuel power plants in many situations even without tax credits. Due to the variable nature of renewable generation, interest in electric storage has soared and we are now seeing grid storage projects being implemented in such numbers that it is feasible to consider a future where electric storage will be a fundamental part of the grid. Meanwhile research continues to try to address the environmental impacts of fossil fuel generation, and a new coal IGCC plant and a new traditional coal unit with stack-based carbon capture have recently been completed. While such demonstration projects are very expensive, if development of the technology results in cost reductions, the ability to economically control carbon emissions could extend the desirability of fossil fuel units well into the future. Two new nuclear units are under construction in the U.S. and will add nuclear capacity that will help offset expected nuclear retirements. But for the long term, many find the concept of small nuclear reactors to be more intriguing than large 2,000 GW projects. While such technology is still well into the future, successful development could result in a resurgence for nuclear power. Other distributed technologies such as fuel cells and small-scale cogeneration could be a part of the future as well. If current trends continue, it appears likely that our future generation mix will be diverse and will include a mix of centralized utility-scale units as well as numerous distributed generation assets located at customer facilities. And over time we will move to a much cleaner generation mix. How quickly this transformation will occur is open to debate.

The Future of Transmission

Until recent years, the U.S. transmission system was fragmented due to its historic construction and operation based on utility service territories, not market conditions or even logical physical flows. With the growth of competitive wholesale markets and large ISOs, the transmission system has become more regionalized in recent years fostering more wholesale trading across large geographic areas. Large ISOs now plan and operate transmission across their market areas without regard to who owns the line. Enhanced utilization of existing lines plus construction of new facilities based on economic value and reduction in congestion has resulted. In 2011, FERC furthered the growth of large transmission market areas with Order 1000, which mandated that all public utilities participate in regional transmission planning processes, that neighboring transmission regions coordinate interregional transmission facilities, and that transmission owners participate in cost allocation methods that foster fair allocation of

YEAR 2050 ENERGY ENVIRONMENT

Fossil fuels no longer dominate
Renewables are important source of world's energy
Electrical system converted to distributed model with significant use of cogeneration and photovoltaic cells
Hydrogen used as energy storage and transport medium
Efficiency of end-use devices has significantly increased
Most of the transport fleet consists of electric vehicles

The world energy mix

Wind — Extensive network of wind farms becomes key source of electricity
Solar — Utility-scale and distributed solar is the cheapest source of electricity
Natural gas — Still used for peaking electricity needs, remainder of resource devoted to hydrogen production
Nuclear — New breed of reactors may become important source of baseload electricity
Hydroelectric — Important electric source for peaking and system support, but environmental concerns and lack of undeveloped resources limit growth
Hydrogen — Hydrogen extracted from water or natural gas using excess renewable energy has replaced oil to fuel transport and has replaced natural gas as fuel for industry

Hydro Dam
Windmills
Hydrogen Pipeline
Hydrogen Production
Fuel Cell
Solar-powered Homes
Factory

supply during hours with large amounts of renewable supply. In the future we may see two sets of system operators: transmission-level ISOs like we have today that will operate the transmission system and foster wholesale markets, and Distribution System Operators or DSOs who will perform a similar function in operating the distribution grid and fostering localized distribution markets.

The Future of Retail Marketing

As of 2019, electric retail marketing is a mature industry in some regions of the country and still unknown in others. Marketers who initially focused on simply trying to win on price or through a few special offerings such as green power are now increasing service options to include energy use analysis, alternative pricing schemes (including free nights and weekends!), help with energy efficiency, and bundling with other home services. Coupled with technological changes that are opening up the market for demand side management, home automation, real-time energy monitoring, and highly efficient and clean distributed generation, this evolution is likely to lead to completely new business models. The retail energy business may evolve to one based on services designed to sell specific value to customers. Customers may buy units of hot water, conditioned air, light, and appliance power from retail marketers who worry about how to efficiently create this value. Others may buy packaged distributed energy resources services that allow them to become prosumers and create a new revenue source from their home. Imagine a future where you buy hot water, comfortable room temperatures, light, appliance power, cable TV, on-demand movies, high-speed internet access, and electric vehicle charging all at one fixed price that is charged to your Starbucks credit card (which of course provides discounts on your coffee purchases). Or one in which you get free Starbucks cards in return for providing distributed energy resources to the grid. Now that may get consumers excited about electric deregulation!

The Future of the Utility

For Baby Boomers growing up in the 1960s and 70s, phone service meant one thing — the service delivered by the local Bell company through copper lines connected to the house. Ask any millennial what a Bell company is and they will probably look at you with a blank face. Arguably, kids born today will have the same reaction when their millennial parents talk to them about the electric utility company.

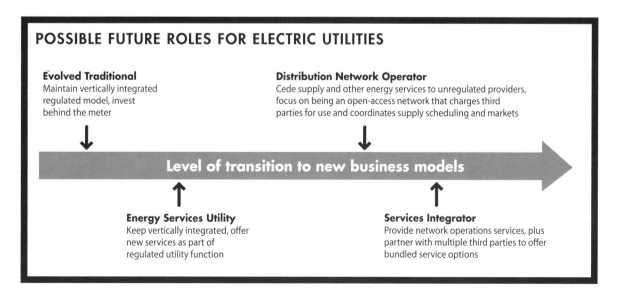

POSSIBLE FUTURE ROLES FOR ELECTRIC UTILITIES

Evolved Traditional
Maintain vertically integrated regulated model, invest behind the meter

Distribution Network Operator
Cede supply and other energy services to unregulated providers, focus on being an open-access network that charges third parties for use and coordinates supply scheduling and markets

Level of transition to new business models

Energy Services Utility
Keep vertically integrated, offer new services as part of regulated utility function

Services Integrator
Provide network operations services, plus partner with multiple third parties to offer bundled service options

New business and regulatory paradigms likely will arise with the growth of distributed energy resources such as rooftop solar, demand side management, and customer-owned storage; the potential growth of a substantial new load in electric vehicles; and third parties such as Apple, Google, and Tesla tinkering with offering customer-oriented energy services. The old business models that have worked for the last 100 years likely will not be sufficient to maintain success in the future, and utilities that survive will be radically transformed. They will have to find new ways of delivering services and making money from them, and regulators will need to adapt regulatory rules to match market realities.

Future customers will expect very different services from what they get today, technologies will radically change the nature of electric generation and delivery, new players will be offering energy services directly to consumers, and entities that deliver services will make money in a different way from today's highly regulated cost-of-service utilities.

A Sustainable Energy Future?

Most believe that eventually our society must transition to an energy future that is based on non-fossil fuels, although debate exists on whether that is in the near future or decades away. The key is to come up with sustainable sources of electricity that are friendly to the environment yet still cost-effective.

One potential scenario (illustrated on page 212) would replace today's centralized electric generation system with a more distributed system based on fuel cells and solar energy located at end-use locations coupled with a fleet of nuclear and renewable utility-scale generators. Automobiles would also be powered by fuel cells and might even act as home generators when parked in the garage. Wind and photovoltaic resources would contribute clean power, and natural gas-fired generation may become a source used only for peaks. Hydrogen might be created from water using energy sources such as wind power or new-generation nuclear. Hydrogen might also be created from natural gas at the wellhead, and the current natural gas pipeline infrastructure could be upgraded to transport hydrogen. Hydrogen would then be piped to end users as a replacement for natural gas and petroleum and as a fuel for the ubiquitous fuel cells.

In the meantime, we must find a way to bridge the gap between today's world and the long-term future. Short-term changes will likely come through a combination of technology evolution and increased efficiency of electric use by the consumer. Technology changes that look promising include ongoing growth of renewable generation, new processes for reducing emissions by fossil fuels, continued improvements in end-use energy efficiency, and development of electricity storage. In addition to the continued evolution of technology, changes in regulation and markets to reward reduced emissions and enhanced energy efficiency are likely.

Electricity is evolving toward a new industry paradigm. As the industry evolves, there is no doubt that it will continue to be marked with revolutionary change. The future will be driven by the creativity and knowledge of individuals who expend the time to become experts not only in the electricity industry but also in broader areas of sustainable development and servicing customer needs through continual innovation.

APPENDIX A: GLOSSARY

Advanced Metering Infrastructure (AMI) — An integrated system of smart meters, communications networks, and data management systems that enables two-way communication between utilities and customers.

Aggregator — An entity that contracts with multiple end-use customers and combines their load into one block of demand in wholesale markets (either for the purpose of serving that load with supply, or in electricity markets, for providing a block of load management resources). Or an entity that collects smaller packages of gas from producers and markets them in larger packages.

Alternating current (AC) — An electric current that reverses its direction in a conductor at regular time intervals.

Amps — Abbreviation of ampere, the unit of measure commonly used to express the rate of current flow in an electric circuit.

Ancillary services — The services in addition to electric supply that are required to deliver electricity to end users and to maintain system reliability. These include automatic generation control (also known as frequency regulation), reserves, voltage support, and blackstart.

Apparent power — The amount of power that comprises both real and reactive power, measured in volt-amps (VA), kilovolt-amps (kVA), or megavolt-amps (MVA).

Automatic Meter Reading (AMR) — The process of collecting meter data remotely through an automated communications system.

Backup generator — A generating unit that is used only when the primary source of power is unavailable.

Balancing Authority — An entity responsible for scheduling electric supply to match forecasted demand, maintaining supply/demand balance within a specific region called the Balancing Authority Area, and maintaining frequency within acceptable tolerances at interconnections with other areas.

Balancing power — See imbalance energy.

Baseload — Electricity usage that is constant through a specified time period. Also used to refer to the generating units that run all 24 hours of the day to serve a system's baseload demand.

Battery — A device that converts chemical energy directly to electric energy from substances contained within one or more battery cells.

Bilateral contract — An agreement between two private parties.

Blackout — The loss of power to a portion of the distribution or transmission system.

Blackstart — Generation that can start up without energy from the grid.

Broker — A third party that earns a profit by matching a buyer and a seller of commodities such as gas or electricity. Unlike marketers, brokers do not take ownership of the commodity.

Bundled service — Gas or electric commodity and distribution service packaged together in a single transaction. Usually provided by the utility.

Capacity — The maximum electric power output of a generating unit (measured in MW) or the maximum amount of power that lines or equipment can safely carry. Also generation that is available to ensure reliability.

Capacity payment — A payment for making generation capacity available to another party.

Carbon dioxide (CO_2) — A by-product of fossil fuel combustion and also an impurity sometimes found in natural gas. Carbon dioxide is a significant greenhouse gas.

Carbon sequestration — The capture and storage of carbon as an approach to reducing greenhouse gas emissions during the power generation process.

Centralized generation — Generation connected to the high voltage electric transmission grid.

Certificate case — Regulatory proceeding held to approve or deny construction of new facilities as requested by utilities.

Circuit — A complete path through which electricity travels, comprising sources of electrons, energy consuming devices, and conductors.

Circuit breaker — A device that interrupts electricity flow to a circuit by isolating the circuit from the source of electricity.

Coal — A combustible fossil fuel that is a mineral solid consisting mostly of carbonized vegetable matter found in underground deposits.

Cogeneration — The use of fuel to produce electricity as well as another product such as steam or hot water.

Combined-cycle gas turbine (CCGT) — A technology for generation that uses a fuel to drive two types of turbines in succession: a combustion turbine and a steam turbine.

Combined heat and power (CHP) — A plant designed to produce both heat and electricity from a single fuel source.

Combustion turbine (CT) — A generation technology that uses air and gaseous fuel to drive a gas turbine, also known as a single-cycle gas turbine.

Commercial customer — An end user that uses power to create a service. Sometimes also used by utilities to refer to manufacturing customers smaller than 500 kW.

Commodity — A standardized product or service that is easily traded among market participants. Also used to refer to electric supply.

Complaint case — A regulatory proceeding held to evaluate a complaint that a utility failed to properly follow regulatory rules.

Conductor — A material through which electricity can flow.

Congestion — A condition that occurs when the amount of requested transactions across a transmission path exceeds the physical capacity of that path.

Congestion cost — The cost for a market participant in an ISO to utilize a congested path.

Congestion management — The process of allocating transmission capacity when congestion occurs.

Control area operator — The entity that performs system operations in a specific region, also called system operator.

Co-op — See Rural electric co-op.

Cost of capital proceeding — The regulatory process that sets the authorized return on debt and return on equity for a utility company. The authorized returns are used in the utility's ratemaking process.

Cost of service — The total amount of money, including return on invested capital, operation and maintenance costs, administrative costs, taxes, and depreciation expense required to provide a utility service.

Cost-of-service regulation — A regulatory methodology that allows utilities to charge rates designed to collect revenues equivalent to their cost of service.

Counterparty — One of the participants in a financial contract.

Creditworthiness — An evaluation of a customer's or trading partner's financial accountability.

Current — The rate of flow of electrons through a conductor.

Customer charge — A fixed amount paid by a customer regardless of actual demand or electric consumption.

Customer choice — The ability of an end-use customer to choose its electricity supplier.

Customer class — A group of end users with similar characteristics, used to segment customers for the purpose of setting rates.

Decoupling — A regulatory methodology that removes the financial impact of throughput or usage on some or all of a utility's revenues. Decoupling removes some or all revenue risk by tracking revenues that differ from authorized revenues and adjusting future rates so that utilities receive, and customers pay, only the authorized amount.

Demand — The total amount of electricity used at any given moment in time, usually measured in kW or MW.

Demand charge — The portion of a rate that is based on the maximum demand recorded over a specified period of time.

Demand curve — A graph showing demand plotted across time.

Demand response (DR) — The act of shifting loads from one time period to another in response to an incentive.

Demand side management (DSM) — The act of reducing energy use or moving energy use from peak to off-peak periods to reduce overall energy costs.

Deregulation — The process of decreasing or eliminating government regulatory control over industries and allowing competitive forces to drive the market.

Direct current (DC) — An electric current that flows in one direction only.

Distributed energy resource (DER) — An electricity supply resource that is either behind a meter on a customer premise or connected to a utility distribution system.

Distributed generation (DG) — Generation located at an end-use customer's facility.

Distribution — The delivery of electricity over medium- and low-voltage lines to consumers of the electricity.

Divestiture — The selling of assets by a regulated utility as part of deregulation.

Economic demand response — Programs that offer end-use customers the opportunity to modify their electric usage in response to wholesale market price signals.

Electric co-op — See rural electric co-op.

Electrical power — The rate of work that can be accomplished by electricity. Commonly measured in units of watts, kilowatts, or megawatts.

Electricity — The flow of electrons through a conductor.

End user — The ultimate consumer of electricity.

Energy — The capacity for performing work. On the electric system this is defined as demand over time measured in kWh or MWh.

Energy efficiency — The act of using less electricity to perform the same amount of work or to get the same end value.

Energy services company (ESCO) — A company that provides services to end users relating to their energy usage. Common services include energy efficiency and demand side management. In New York this term is also used to describe a retail marketer.

Fault — A failure or interruption in an electrical circuit.

Federal Energy Regulatory Commission (FERC) — The federal body that regulates wholesale electric services.

Federal power agency — An agency of the U.S. government that markets the output of generating units owned by the federal government.

Financial services company — An entity that provides risk management and financing services.

Financial transmission right (FTR) — A right to receive financial compensation for the difference between actual congestion costs and the price of the FTR.

Firm service — Supply or transmission service that is expected to always be available except during operational problems.

Forward market — A market where delivery of the item purchased is at some future point in time. In electric markets the delivery is at least two days after the date of purchase.

Fossil fuel — Any fuel created by the decomposition of organic matter including natural gas, oil, and coal.

Frequency — How often the direction of flow reserves in an A.C. circuit, commonly measured in Hz.

Frequency support — The use of electric resources to maintain system frequency at acceptable levels.

Fuel cell — A device that converts stored chemical energy directly to electric energy. Although similar to a battery, the major difference is that a fuel cell operates with a continuous supply of fuel (such as natural gas or hydrogen) as opposed to a battery, which contains a fixed supply of fuel.

Futures contract — A supply contract between a buyer and seller where the buyer is obligated to take delivery and the seller is obligated to provide delivery of a fixed amount of commodity at a predetermined price and location at a specific period in time. Futures are bought and sold through an exchange such as NYMEX.

Generation — The creation of electricity.

Generator — Used synonymously with the term power plant or generating unit (although technically, the generator is the part of the power plant that converts the mechanical power of a spinning shaft to electricity).

Geothermal — Heat extracted from reservoirs in the earth.

Global warming — The warming of the earth's atmosphere due to increased concentrations of greenhouse gases.

Green power — Electricity generated using renewable fuels, usually excluding large hydro power.

Greenhouse gas — A gas that contributes to the greenhouse effect. Greenhouse gases include carbon dioxide, methane, ozone, nitrous oxide, and various chlorofluorocarbons.

Grid — Usually used to describe the interconnected transmission system, although sometimes used with distribution (distribution grid) to describe the distribution system.

Heat rate — The amount of fuel required to generate a specified amount of electricity, usually expressed in terms of Btu/kWh.

Hedge — The initiation of a transaction in a physical or financial market to reduce risk.

High voltage direct current transmission (HVDC) lines — Transmission lines that use DC power instead of AC, with a voltage of 200 kV or higher.

Hub — A physical location where multiple transmission lines interconnect and where buyers and sellers can make transactions.

Hydro power — Electricity generated by water falling across a water turbine.

Imbalance — The discrepancy between the amount of electricity an entity delivers into the grid and the actual amount the entity consumes.

Imbalance energy — Power purchased by the system operator during the hour to keep the system supply in balance with demand.

Incentive ratemaking — A form of ratemaking that rewards utility shareholders for achieving goals set by the regulator.

Independent power producer (IPP) — A generation company that is not part of a regulated vertically integrated utility company that sells output under a long-term contract.

Independent System Operator (ISO) — An independent entity that provides system operation functions including managing system reliability and transmission access.

Index — A calculated number designed to represent the average price of electricity bought and sold at a specific location during a specified period of time.

Industrial customer — An end user that uses power for manufacturing or production of a product. Sometimes defined by utilities simply by size — bigger than 500 kW demand is a common minimum size.

Insulator — A material with high resistance to electricity, meaning that electricity cannot easily travel through it.

Integrated gas combined-cycle (IGCC) — A power plant that takes solid coal, converts it into synthetic gas, and then uses the gas to power a combined-cycle gas turbine.

Integrated resource planning (IRP) — The process by which a utility forecasts future demand, evaluates all its options for satisfying that demand, and then develops a plan for serving it.

Interconnection — The facilities where a generator connects to the electric grid or where two electric lines are connected.

Interruptible rates — An electric rate schedule whereby the end-use customer agrees to not use power during certain hours when instructed by the system operator (used by the system operator as a means of maintaining reliability). In return, the customer receives a rate discount.

Inverter — A device that converts direct current (DC) electricity to alternating current (AC).

Investor-owned utility (IOU) — A regulated monopoly utility that is owned by shareholders and run as a for-profit entity.

kW — Kilowatt.

kWh — Kilowatt-hour.

Load — An amount of end-use demand.

Load center — A location on an electrical grid where there is a large amount of load, typically requiring that electricity be moved into the location by transmission lines.

Load factor — The amount of electricity used by a consumer over a period of time divided by the amount of energy they would have used had they continuously consumed energy over the period at their maximum demand level

Load Serving Entity (LSE) — An entity that sells electric supply to an end user.

Locational marginal pricing (LMP) — A method of setting prices in an ISO market whereby prices at specific locations on the grid are determined by the marginal price of generation of power available to that specific location. Prices vary from location to location based on transmission congestion and losses.

Loop flow — Flow of electricity that follows the path of least resistance on the transmission grid. The actual path may include parallel paths around the assumed contractual path.

Market-based rates — Charges for regulated services that are determined by market forces rather than being set by the regulator.

Market power — The ability of a market participant to artificially elevate prices over a period of time.

Marketer — An entity that buys electricity, arranges for its transmission, and then resells the electricity to end users or other electricity buyers.

Merchant generator — A generation unit or company that is not part of a regulated monopoly utility and that is subject to market pricing for sales.

Meter — A device used to measure the amount of electricity flowing through a point on the system.

Monopoly — A marketplace characterized by only one seller.

Muni — See municipal utility.

Municipal utility — A utility owned and operated by a municipality.

Native load — The end-use customer load of a specific utility.

Natural gas — A combustible gaseous mixture of simple hydrocarbon compounds, primarily methane.

Nitrogen oxides (NO_x) — A group of highly reactive gases consisting of one nitrogen molecule and two or more oxygen molecules; a significant contributor to the formation of ground level ozone which can cause smog.

North American Electric Reliability Corporation (NERC) — An international, independent, self-regulated, not-for-profit organization whose mission is to promulgate electric operation and planning standards and ensure the reliability of the bulk power system in North America.

Notice of Proposed Rulemaking (NOPR) — A document released by a regulatory agency in which the agency sets forth a proposed revision to its rules and gives market participants notice concerning the regulatory proceeding that will consider these revised rules.

Nuclear power — Electricity generated using the heat of nuclear fission.

Off-peak — The hours during the day when demand is at its lowest.

Open access — The requirement that a transmission system transmit electricity for any creditworthy party on a non-discriminatory basis.

Option — A contract that gives the holder the right, but not the obligation, to purchase or sell a commodity at a specific price within a specified time period in return for a premium payment.

Organized wholesale markets — Wholesale markets where the purchase and sale of energy and energy services are facilitated by an ISO or power exchange.

Output — The amount of energy put onto the grid by a power plant over a specific period of time, usually measured in MWh.

Overhead facilities — Electrical facilities that are installed on transmission towers or distribution poles.

Peak — The hours during the day when demand is at its highest.

Peak demand — The maximum demand for electricity in a given period of time.

Peaking units — Generating units run only during times of peak demand on a system.

Performance-based ratemaking (PBR) — A form of incentive ratemaking in which a utility's actual performance (either financial or service-wise) is compared against specified baselines. The utility can attain extra earnings if the baseline is exceeded but can lose earnings if the baseline is not achieved.

Photovoltaic (PV) cell — A cell containing material that converts light into electricity.

Power — See Electrical power. Power is synonymous with demand in kW or MW. Also a synonym for electricity.

Power exchange (PX) — An independent entity that establishes a centralized spot market for day-ahead or hour-ahead electric markets.

Power plant — A combination of connected generators and other equipment that produces electric power. Synonymous with generating unit.

Power pool — An entity formed by multiple utilities to coordinate dispatch of generating units owned by the utilities to optimize coordinated system operations among the utilities.

Power purchase agreement (PPA) — A contract for the sale/purchase of electricity.

Power quality — A measure of the level of voltage and/or frequency disturbances.

Price volatility — The movement of market prices over time.

Primary distribution — A voltage (ranging from 600 volts to 50 kV) on the distribution system that is lower than transmission voltage and higher than secondary voltage. Common voltages include 4160V, 12.5 kV, 25 kV, 36 kV.

Public Service Commission (PSC) — The state agency that regulates the activities of investor-owned utilities (and also municipal utilities in some states).

Public utility — A regulated entity that supplies the general public with an essential service such as electricity, natural gas, water, or telephone.

Public Utility Commission (PUC) — See Public Service Commission.

Public utility district (PUD) — A utility run by a local governmental agency or a group of governmental agencies other than a municipality.

Ramp rate — The speed at which a power plant can increase its power output, usually stated in terms of MW per minute.

Rate — A regulated price charged by a regulated entity such as a utility.

Rate base — The net investment in facilities, equipment, and other property a utility has constructed or purchased to provide utility services to its customers.

Rate case — The regulatory proceeding in which a utility's rates are determined.

Rate design — The development and structure of rates for regulated electric services.

Rate of return on equity (ROE) — Earnings divided by the equity portion of the rate base. ROE can be stated as actual ROE, which is based on actual earnings, or authorized ROE, which is the return authorized by the regulator during a cost of capital proceeding and used to set rates.

Rate of return — overall (ROR) — The amount of revenue left to pay debt and earnings after all expenses, taxes, and depreciation have been paid divided by the size of the rate base.

Rate schedule — The commission-approved document setting out rates and terms of service specific to a certain service and service provider.

Rated capacity — The maximum power in MW that a power plant is designed to provide to the grid without reducing its design life.

Reactive power — The form of electric power that is measured in volt-amps reactive (VAR), kilovolt-amps reactive (kVAR), or megavolt-amps reactive (MVAR).

Real power — The form of electric power that is measured in watts (W), kilowatts (kW) or megawatts (MW).

Reciprocating engine — An engine that converts pressure to rotating movement by using pistons to turn a crankshaft.

Regional transmission organization (RTO) — An ISO that operates over a regional geographical area and fits specific criteria defined by FERC.

Regulation — The multitude of rules or orders issued by state or federal agencies that dictate how electric service is provided to customers. Also used in system operations to describe ramping a generating unit up or down to match supply to demand in real time.

Regulator — The governmental entity that sets the rules and orders that make up regulation.

Renewable energy — Electricity that is generated from a source that is naturally replenished in a reasonably short period of time such as solar, wind, geothermal, biomass, and hydro. The term sometimes excludes large-scale hydro due to assumed environmental impacts of these projects.

Renewable fuel — A fuel that is naturally replenished such as wind or solar.

Renewable Portfolio Standard (RPS) — A regulatory or legislative rule that requires utility companies and other load serving entities to source a certain amount of the energy they generate or sell from renewable sources.

Reliability — A measure of how often electrical service is interrupted.

Reserves — Generation capacity that is available to the system operator if needed but that is not currently generating electricity.

Residential customer — An end user that uses power in a home.

Resources — The amount of available electricity capacity in a specific region or market.

Restructuring — Changes in regulatory rules that result in change in control, ownership or regulatory mechanisms applicable to specific industry sectors.

Retail access — The opportunity for an end user to buy electric supply from someone other than his regulated utility distribution company.

Retail competition — The opportunity for multiple electric suppliers to compete to sell electric supply service to end-use customers.

Retail marketer — A firm that sells products and services directly to end users.

Resistance — A measure of the strength of impedance, which is a physical property that slows down the flow of electricity.

Return — The amount of money included in the revenue requirement to provide earnings and/or to pay back debt.

Revenue requirement — The revenues a utility must take in to cover its total estimated costs and allowed return.

Rulemaking — A regulatory proceeding held to establish new market rules.

Rules — Commission-approved general terms of service included in tariffs.

Rural electric co-op — A utility owned by its customers that usually serves rural areas.

Scheduling — The process of determining which generating units will be generating or on reserve status for a specific hour. Also, the process of determining which requested transactions across a transmission line will be allowed to occur.

Secondary distribution — A voltage on the distribution system that is at the level typically used by customers such as 120V, 208V, 240V, 277V, 480V, or 2,400V.

Service territory — The geographical area served by a utility.

Service voltage — The voltage delivered by the utility to a customer facility.

Short circuit — An interruption in the flow of electricity due to an undesired conductor coming in contact with the electrical flow.

Smart grid — Transmission and distribution system integrating modern digital technologies to enhance monitoring, communication, control, and support systems.

Smart meter — An advanced solid state meter that includes remote communication of data and may also provide remote control capabilities.

Solar power — Electricity generated using the power of the sun; includes photovoltaic power and concentrated solar power (CSP).

Speculating — The initiation of a transaction in a physical or financial market with the goal of making a profit due to market movement.

Spot market — The short-term market for electricity — usually refers to day-ahead, hour-ahead, and real-time markets.

Steam turbine — A turbine whose blades are spun by the kinetic energy in moving steam.

Storage — The capture of electrical energy produced at one time for use at a later time.

Stranded costs — Utility costs that result from assets acquired under prior regulatory rules that are in excess of the market value of those assets.

Substation — A facility containing switches, transformers, and other equipment used to adjust voltages and monitor circuits.

Sulfur dioxide (SO_2) — A gas made of sulfur and oxygen that is a significant contributor to the formation of acid rain.

Supply — Electricity available to the grid.

System operator — The entity that manages the transmission grid by dispatching generation and scheduling reserves and transmission.

System peak — The maximum load on an electrical system during a given period of time.

Tariffs — All effective rate schedules for a utility along with the general terms and conditions of service.

Time-of-use (TOU) rate — A method of charging electric rates based on the time of day that the energy is used.

Trading arrangements — The set of rules that specify how the system operator will acquire the necessary services to maintain system reliability and will allocate transmission access.

Transformer — A device used to change voltage. A step-up transformer increases the voltage while a step-down transformer decreases it.

Transco — The abbreviation for transmission company, a regulated entity that owns only transmission facilities.

Transmission — The transport of electricity over high voltage power lines from generators to the interconnection with the distribution system.

Transmission line — A power line with a voltage greater than 50 kV or 50,000 volts.

Transmission owner (TO) — The entity that owns a transmission line or transmission system.

Turbine — A machine with blades that are rotated by the movement of liquid or gas thus converting the kinetic energy of the liquid to mechanical energy of a rotating shaft.

Unbundling — The separation of an electric utility's distribution service from electric supply service.

Underground facilities — Electrical facilities that are installed below ground level.

Usage — The same as energy in kWh or MWh.

Usage charge — A rate charge that is based on the amount of kWh consumed over a given period of time.

Utility distribution company (UDC) — A regulated utility that provides distribution services to end users.

Value-added services — Services related to electrical supply that are in addition to supply itself.

Value at Risk (VAR) — A measure of potential earnings loss due to adverse market movements with a specified probability over a particular period of time.

Vertical integration — The ownership of all sectors of electric delivery (generation, transmission, system operations, and distribution) within one entity.

Volatility — See Price volatility.

Volt — A unit of measure of voltage.

Volt-amps reactive (VAR) — A unit of measure of reactive power.

Voltage — The electrical pressure that moves electricity through conductors.

Voltage support — The use of electric resources or grid devices to maintain voltage at acceptable levels.

Wheeling — The transmission of power across a utility system on behalf of a marketer or generator.

Wholesale trading — The buying and selling of power between parties that are not ultimate end users.

Wind turbine — A turbine that is spun by the kinetic energy in wind.

A

B

APPENDIX B: UNITS AND CONVERSIONS

Mcf = thousand cubic feet

MMcf = million cubic feet

Btu = British thermal unit

MMBtu = million Btu

GJ = gigajoule (metric measure of energy)

Dth = decatherm

kW = kilowatt

kWh = kilowatt hour

MW = megawatt

MWh = megawatt hour

1 therm = 100,000 Btu

1 Dth = 10 therms

10 therms = 1 MMBtu

1,000,000 Btu = 1 MMBtu

1 Dth = 1 MMBtu

1000 Mcf = 1 MMcf

1000 MMcf = 1 Bcf

1 MMcf = 1,015 MMBtu*

1 GJ = 0.95 MMBtu

1000 kWh = 1 MWh

1000 kW = 1 MW

*This conversion varies with the energy content of the gas

C

$$\boxed{\text{C}}$$

APPENDIX C: ACRONYMS

A — Amp

AC — Alternating current

AGC — Automatic generation control

ALJ — Administrative Law Judge

AMI — Advanced metering infrastructure

AMR — Automated meter reading

BPA — Bonneville Power Administration

Btu — British thermal unit

CAISO — California Independent System Operator

CCGT — Combined-cycle gas turbine

CHP — Combined heat and power

CO$_2$ — Carbon dioxide

COB — California-Oregon border

CPUC — California Public Utilities Commission

CSP — Concentrated solar power

CT — Combustion turbine

DC — Direct current

DER — Distributed energy resource

DG — Distributed generation

DOE — U.S. Department of Energy

DR — Demand response

DSM — Demand side management

Dth — Decatherm

EE — Energy efficiency

EDR — Economic demand response

EIA — Energy Information Administration

EIM — Energy imbalance market

EMF — Electromagnetic field

EMS — Energy management system

EPA — Environmental Protection Agency

EPMC — Equal proportionate marginal costs

ERCOT — Electric Reliability Council of Texas

ERO — Electric reliability organization

ESCO — Energy services company

ESP — Energy services provider

EV — Electric vehicle

EWG — Exempt wholesale generator

FERC — Federal Energy Regulatory Commission

FPA — Federal Power Act

FPC — Federal Power Commission

FRCC — Florida Reliability Coordinating Council

FTC — Federal Trade Commission

FTR — Financial transmission rights

GNP — Gross national product

GW — Gigawatt

GWh — Gigawatt-hour

HVAC — Heating ventilating and air conditioning

HVDC — High voltage direct current

Hz — Hertz

ICE — Intercontinental Exchange

IGCC — Integrated gasification combined-cycle

IOU — Investor-owned utility

IPP — Independent power producer

IRP — Integrated resource plan

ISO — Independent System Operator

ISO-NE — ISO New England

kV — Kilovolt

kVA — Kilovolt-ampere

kVAR — Kilovolt-ampere reactive

kW — Kilowatt

kWh — Kilowatt-hour

LMP — Locational marginal pricing

LSE — Load Serving Entity

MAPP — Mid-Continent Area Power Pool

MISO — Midcontinent ISO

MMBtu — Million British thermal units

MRO — Midwest Reliability Organization

Muni — Municipal utility

MW — Megawatt

MWh — Megawatt-hour

NERC — North American Electric Reliability Corporation

NIMBY — Not in my backyard

NOPR — Notice of Proposed Rulemaking

NOx — Nitrogen oxide

NPCC — Northeast Power Coordinating Council

NRC — Nuclear Regulatory Commission

NUG — Non-utility generator

NYMEX — New York Mercantile Exchange

O&M — Operations and maintenance

OAT — Open access transmission

OTC — Over-the-counter

PBR — Performance-based ratemaking

PJM — Pennsylvania-New Jersey-Maryland ISO

POLR — Provider of last resort

PSC — Public Service Commission

PUC — Public Utility Commission

PUHCA — Public Utilities Holding Company Act of 1935

PUD — Public utilities district

PURPA — Public Utilities Regulatory Policy Act of 1978

PV — Photovoltaic

PX — Power exchange

QF — Qualifying facility

R&D — Research and development

REA — Rural electric agency

REC — Retail electric company

RFC — ReliabilityFirst Corporation

ROE — Return on equity

ROR — Rate of return

RPS — Renewable portfolio standard

RTO — Regional transmission organization

SCADA — Supervisory control and data acquisition

SEC — Securities and Exchange Commission

SERC — SERC Reliability Corporation

SEPA — Southeastern Power Administration

SMD — Standard Market Design

SO_2 — Sulfur dioxide

SPP — Southwest Power Pool

SWPA — Southwestern Power Administration

TCC — Transmission congestion contract

TCR — Transmission congestion right

TLR — Transmission loading relief

TO — Transmission owner

TOU — Time of use

TRE — Texas Reliability Entity

TVA — Tennessee Valley Authority

UDC — Utility distribution company

UPS — Uninterruptible power supply

V — Volt

VAR — Value at Risk; also volt-ampere reactive

WAPA — Western Area Power Administration

WECC — Western Electricity Coordinating Council

D

APPENDIX D: INDEX

D

D